Clues to Comprehension
Building Strategic Thinking Skills Through Language

Program Overview

"Case" Posters

In *Clues to Comprehension*, 40 posters provide "cases" to solve that engage students in critical and deductive thinking as they try to determine the identity of the "mystery item" that is the subject of each poster. The mystery items are presented on posters featuring ads for lost and found items, "help wanted" and "job wanted" ads, and "for sale" ads.

Found!
August 8th on sidewalk. Rectangular green and white paper item with the number "1" in all four corners. Picture of George Washington on the front, an eagle on the back. Call I.M. Honest at 555-8183 if you can prove it's yours.

CASE # 6

What did I.M. Honest find?

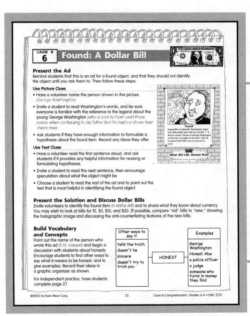

Teacher Pages

For each poster, an accompanying teacher's page provides guidelines for modeling and practicing critical-thinking strategies. As you conduct these lessons, encourage students to explain the thinking behind their responses. Accept all answers that can be logically substantiated by students, even though they may at first appear to be incorrect or inaccurate. It may turn out that a student is thinking "outside the box" or using a perspective that may be different from yours and other students'.

Student Pages

A reproducible student page is also included for each of the 40 lessons. These pages use item formats similar to those found on many standardized language skills tests, and include skills such as vocabulary development, reading comprehension, decoding, and structural analysis.

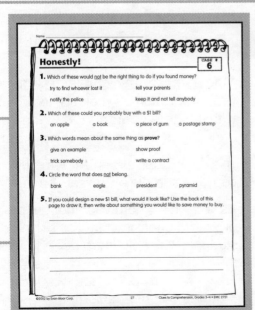

Teacher Pages Model Thinking and Learning Strategies

Model Use of Picture Clues

As you guide students through the steps in the **Use Picture Clues** section, model how to work with the nontext clues provided in the illustrations. Encourage students to focus first on the illustration—not the text—and to use logic and deductive reasoning to support their hypotheses.

Confirm Solutions and Share Information

As you move into the **Present the Solution** section, encourage students to share information on the subject under discussion. To ensure best use of discussion time, establish guidelines for participating in class discussions. These might include:

- Raise your hand and wait to be recognized before speaking.
- Give others your full attention while they are speaking.
- Respect everybody's right to hold individual opinions, whether you agree with them or not.
- Try to support your statements with examples or logic.

Model Use of Text Clues

As you lead students through the steps outlined under **Use Text Clues**, encourage students to use new information to revise their hypotheses. Again, always have students explain their reasoning, and accept all answers that can be supported with logic.

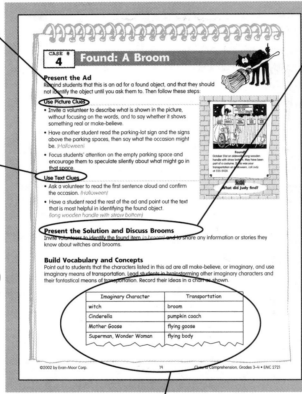

Model Critical Thinking with Graphic Organizers

Graphic organizers make critical thinking "visible" for students. By using "think-alouds" as you work with the graphic organizers in the **Build Vocabulary and Concepts** activities, you can help students understand how to think about organizing, interpreting, and understanding information.

Use the graphic organizer templates provided on pages 134–142 to create overhead transparencies, or copy the sample organizers on the teacher pages onto the board or chart paper.

As you write, share your thought process with students by talking through the reasoning behind the organizational structure you are modeling. When you make your thinking explicit by verbalizing it to students, you help them begin to internalize principles for organizing information. As you progress through the lessons, encourage students to suggest organizational structures. Ask questions such as, *"If we want to look at the way two things are similar and different, what would be a good way to organize our information?"*

Student Pages Provide Practice with Test-Taking Skills

The activities on the reproducible student pages use the content of the posters as a springboard to related language arts activities. Activity formats emulate many of the typical item formats found on standardized language tests. You can help students feel prepared and confident when they encounter items of this type by modeling and reviewing strategies for approaching each type of activity. See pages 6 and 7 for tips on teaching the following skills, which are presented on the student pages:

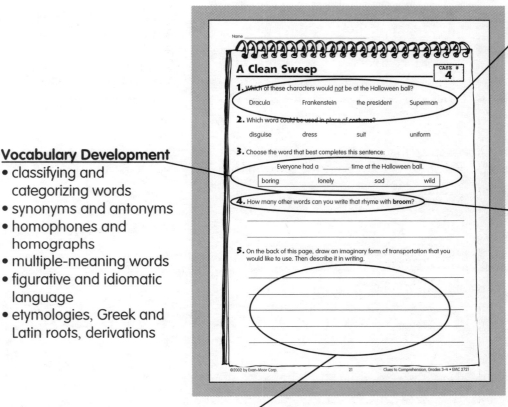

Reading Comprehension
• literal comprehension, details
• drawing conclusions
• making inferences and generalizations
• analyzing, evaluating, and synthesizing information

Decoding and Structural Analysis
• spelling patterns
• rhyming words
• prefixes and suffixes

Vocabulary Development
• classifying and categorizing words
• synonyms and antonyms
• homophones and homographs
• multiple-meaning words
• figurative and idiomatic language
• etymologies, Greek and Latin roots, derivations

Open-Ended Exercises

On each activity page, there is also an open-ended item that invites students to draw and write in response to a prompt. Drawing first helps students focus their thoughts in a way that is usually nonthreatening. Then when students are asked to write about their picture, they already have a visual guide to help get them started in their writing. Use the writing samples to track the aspects of writing that you wish to evaluate or focus on for individual or group instruction.

> See page 8 for ideas for meeting the needs of students acquiring English and accelerated and struggling learners.

©2002 by Evan-Moor Corp. Clues to Comprehension, Grades 3–4 • EMC 2721

About the CD-ROM

Loading the Program

1 Put the CD in your CD drive.

This CD-ROM contains both Windows and MacOS programs.

Your computer will recognize the correct program.

2 On some computers, the program will automatically start up. If the program does not start automatically:

Windows—go to My Computer, double click on the CD drive, then double click on Begin.exe.

MacOS—double click on the CD icon on your desktop, then double click on Begin.

3 After the program starts, you will arrive at the main menu.

Main Menu Features

The 40 "cases" found in the book are presented in full-color with an interactive element. To present a whole-class lesson, connect your computer to a projection system. As a review, students may be taught to access a specific case during their computer time.

○ Choose a Topic

1 Click on **Choose a Topic** to display the list of categories.

2 Click on a topic. The topic will be displayed, along with case numbers.

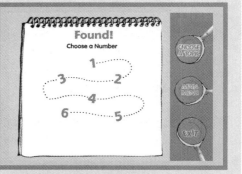

3 Click on a case number. The case will be displayed, followed by a full-color illustration case poster from the book. For example, **Case #1, What did Sean find?**

④

Refer to Case #1 in the workbook, **Found: A Compass**.

Click on the beneath the image.

The descriptive clues accompanying the illustration will be displayed. The clues are revealed following the directions sequence in the **Use Text Clues** section on the teacher page in the book.

⑤

After discussing the clues and possible solutions, click on  to reveal the answer.

⑥

You may then click on  to select the next case number, and repeat steps #3 through #5,

or you may click on to select another category, or click on to close the program.

◯ View the E-Book

• The teacher pages, clue charts, activity pages, and answer key are presented in a printable electronic format. You must have Adobe® Acrobat® Reader™ installed to access the e-book. (See installation instructions below.)

Installing Adobe® Acrobat® Reader™
You need to have Acrobat Reader installed on your computer to access the e-book portion of the CD-ROM. If you do not have Acrobat Reader, go to the main menu of the CD and follow these instructions:

1. Place your cursor over the Click Here link. Wait for the hand and then click.
2. When you see the Acrobat Reader Setup Screen, click the "Next" box.
3. When you see the Destination Location Screen, click the "Next" box.
4. When you see the Setup Complete Screen, click "finish."

Your system will now shut down to finish the installation process. Some systems will automatically restart. If yours does not, start it up manually.

• You may scroll through the entire book page by page or open the "Bookmarks" tab for a clickable table of contents.

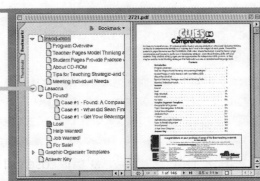

Hint: This symbol, ⊞ for Windows or ▷ for MacOS, means that you can click there to expand this category.

• To print pages from the e-book, click on the printer icon. A print dialog box will open. Enter the page or pages you wish to print in the print range boxes. (At the bottom of the screen, you can see which page of the e-book you are viewing.)

• To exit the e-book, simply "X" out until you return to the main menu.

 Exit. This button closes the program.

Tips for Teaching Strategic- and Critical-Thinking Skills

Vocabulary Development Activities

Classifying and Categorizing Words

Student activity pages include exercises that require students to identify one word in a group of four that does <u>not</u> fit in the same category as the others. Model the strategy for this sort of exercise by using think-alouds to identify the category and the element that does <u>not</u> fit:

They are all geometric shapes?

We need to find the word that does not belong in this group. First, we need to see what this group is. What group do rectangular, square, triangular, and wide all belong to? You are right: Those words all describe shapes and sizes. But rectangular, square, and triangular are all geometric shapes. Wide describes size, but it is not a geometric shape, so wide does not belong.

Synonyms and Antonyms

To make sure students understand the terms synonym and antonym, define them as "words that mean the same thing" and "words that mean the opposite" of the target words presented in these exercises. Then, use think-alouds to model word-substitution strategies: use the target word in a sentence, then replace it with each of the answer choices to identify the correct response. Use a similar procedure to model how to check whether words are antonyms.

Homophones, Homographs, and Multimeaning Words

You may wish to teach students the Greek words homos (same), phone (sound), and graphos (writing). Then, explain that homophones are words that sound the same, but have different meanings. Homophones may be spelled the same, like a pitcher used to pour water and the pitcher on a baseball team. Homophones may also sound alike but be spelled differently, like beat (a drum) and beet (a root vegetable). When students are searching a text for homophones, remind them to say the words to themselves to help heighten their awareness of matching sounds.

Homographs are words that are spelled the same, but have different meanings. Homographs may sound the same, like ruler (a leader) and ruler (a tool for measuring). Homographs may also be sound different, like wind (the kind that blows) and wind (what you do when you twist a knob). Help students use context clues in the text to decide which meaning is intended, or to replace the word with a synonym to check for sense.

It may help students to use a dictionary as they try to identify additional meanings of homophones or homographs. Students acquiring English may wish to keep individual lists of these challenging words.

Figurative and Idiomatic Language

Idiomatic expressions, puns and humor, and double-entendre can all be difficult to explain and are particularly challenging for English learners. Encourage students to help you brainstorm lots of examples to provide additional context to help them comprehend these expressions. You and your students may enjoy investigating the origins of specific idiomatic expressions; students may wish to keep lists of these expressions, adding definitions or illustrations to clarify meaning.

Analogies

Use think-alouds to model how to identify the relationships between words in these exercises (see Case 2, page 112):

We're looking for words that are related to each other in the same way as breakfast *is related to* morning. Breakfast *is a meal, and* morning *is the time of day when we eat it.* Snack *is a bit of food to eat, and* cookies *are a type of food, so that is* <u>not</u> *a similar relationship.* Dinner *is a meal, and* evening *is the time of day when we eat it, so these two words do have a similar relationship.*

Reading Comprehension Exercises

Student pages include various types of exercises that require students to process information from the poster text in order to answer literal comprehension questions, make generalizations and inferences, and draw conclusions.

Other exercises require students to apply these critical-thinking skills to topics that have been explored during teacher-directed discussions.

In modeling strategies for conducting comprehension activities, use think-alouds to show how to examine each answer option, using critical thinking, deductive reasoning, text clues, and other traditional reading comprehension strategies to select the correct answer choices. Once again, encourage students to support their answer choices with logical reasoning, bearing in mind that students may be able to justify an answer that might otherwise appear to be incorrect to you or other students. (Note that the answer key often specifies "Answers may vary.")

Decoding and Structural Analysis

Rhyming Words

For activities that ask students to write rhyming words, teach students to make alphabet, blend, and digraph strips and model how to use them to find rhyming words as shown at right.

You may also compile the rhyming words recorded by students on their activity pages and display them on bulletin boards or in the writing center as resources for students. Rhyming word collections are especially helpful for writing poetry.

Suffixes and Prefixes

As you work through these exercises with students, you may wish to collect affixes that have similar meanings, such as *dis-*, *in-*, and *un-* for prefixes meaning "not." Display them on a bulletin board or in the writing center.

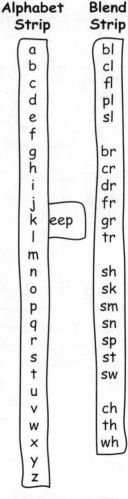

Meeting Individual Needs

Students Acquiring English

Clues to Comprehension can be easily adapted to further enhance acquisition of concepts and vocabulary for students who are acquiring English as a second language.

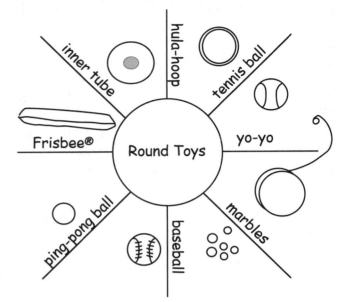

- **Teach Cultural Literacy**—Be sure to include "cultural literacy" instruction in lessons that feature characters from folklore or traditional literature, American holidays, or other elements that may be culture-specific.

- **Provide Visual Clues**—As information is shared during group discussions or as you develop graphic organizers, add simple sketches to help students quickly grasp the meaning of new or unfamiliar words.

- **Highlight Sound/Symbol Correspondence**—Whenever you model writing for students, verbalize each word as you write it. This helps increase students' awareness of the letters that are used to represent particular sounds.

- **Capitalize on Teachable Moments**—Take advantage of any teachable moments that arise to make connections for students. You might refer to vocabulary introduced previously as you explain the meaning of a new synonym. Or, make a point about spelling rules by using a word that comes up to introduce a family of words that all include a unique spelling pattern. Teachable moments are impossible to predict, but invaluable to deepening students' understanding of new concepts, vocabulary, and rules.

Accelerated Learners

As students become proficient in using the various learning strategies to complete the student activity pages, you may allow accelerated learners to move ahead on their own in completing these pages, while you work with a smaller group to focus on identifying and applying learning strategies for each exercise.

Consider these possibilities for extending learning for accelerated students:

- Have students use the rhyming words that they brainstorm to compose a rhyme or poem.

- Write sentences or definitions for the rhyming words that they list.

- Identify the category that items belong to in the categorization activities.

- Invite students to find and explain all puns and humorous references in the poster text.

Struggling Learners

Struggling learners should be supported through ongoing instruction and review of the learning strategies modeled in the program until they feel comfortable using them independently. Encourage struggling writers and English learners to begin by dictating text to accompany their drawings in the open-ended writing activity. They may also add labels to their pictures, then slowly build up to writing simple sentences.

Found!

Found!

October 31st on sidewalk. Long wooden handle with straw bottom. May have been part of a costume. If this was your transportation on Halloween, call Judy at 555-5428.

CASE # 4

What did Judy find?

Found!

July 19th, on trail around lake at Mosquito Bay Campground. Small and round. Shows directions. You must have dropped it while hiking on the path. It helped us locate our campsite. Thanks! Call Sean at 555-6118 to get it back.

CASE # 1

What did Sean find?

Found!

August 8th on sidewalk. Rectangular green and white paper item with the number "1" in all four corners. Picture of George Washington on the front, an eagle on the back. Call I.M. Honest at 555-8183 if you can prove it's yours.

CASE # 6

What did I.M. Honest find?

©2002 by Evan-Moor Corp.

Clues to Comprehension, Grades 3–4 • EMC 2721

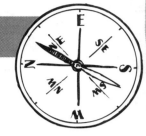

Found: A Compass

CASE # 1

Present the Ad

Tell students that this is an ad for a found object, and that they should not identify the object until you ask them to. Then follow these steps:

Use Picture Clues

- Ask volunteers to name everything in the picture that is part of nature (not made by people). *(clouds, mountains, trees, lake, animals, rocks, plants, stick)*

- Ask students what they think the boy is doing in this natural setting, and what clues in the picture support their ideas. *(hiking; backpack, walking stick)* Then elicit their ideas about what the boy might be reaching for on the path.

Use Text Clues

Ask a volunteer to read the text aloud. Then have students find words that tell

- where the boy is. *(trail, lake, Mosquito Bay Campground)*

- about the item he found. *(small, round, shows directions, helped locate campsite)*

Discuss the different meanings of "directions" *(instructions for doing something; the cardinal directions: north, south, east, and west)*, and determine which meaning is intended in this context.

Found!
July 19th, on trail around lake at Mosquito Bay Campground. Small and round. Shows directions. You must have dropped it while hiking on the path. It helped us locate our campsite. Thanks! Call Sean at 555-6118 to get it back.

CASE # 1
What did Sean find?

©2002 by Evan-Moor Corp.   11   Clues to Comprehension, Grades 3–4 • EMC 2721

Present the Solution and Discuss Compasses

Invite volunteers to identify the found item *(a compass)* and to share what they know about compasses. You may need to explain that compasses are made with magnets, and that the compass needle always points north because of the powerful magnetic field at Earth's North Pole.

Build Vocabulary and Concepts

Use familiar landmarks to help students orient themselves to the cardinal directions: *The Pacific Ocean is in the west, so the west is over in this direction*, etc. Guide students in brainstorming other familiar landmarks and determining their location in relation to your school. Record information on a directional organizer as shown at right.

For independent practice, have students complete page 12.

NORTH		
Alaska		
Canada		
the North Pole		
Washington (state)		

WEST		EAST
Pacific Ocean	New York	
Hawai'i	Europe	
Asia	the library	
the office	teacher's desk	

	Baja California	
	Mexico	
	South America	
	Antarctica	
	SOUTH	

Found!

July 19th, on trail around lake at Mosquito Bay Campground. Small and round. Shows directions. You must have dropped it while hiking on the path. It helped us locate our campsite. Thanks! Call Sean at 555-6118 to get it back.

CASE #
1

What did Sean find?

©2002 by Evan-Moor Corp.

Clues to Comprehension, Grades 3–4 • EMC 2721

Get Your Bearings

1. Circle the word from the ad that means the same thing as **trail**.

    lake   bay   campground   path

2. North is the opposite of south. What is the opposite of **east**?

    up   west   down   right

3. Circle the word that does <u>not</u> belong.

    lake   mountain   backpack   raccoon

4. Choose the word that best completes this sentence:

The needle on a compass always points _____ .

away	down	home	north

5. On the back of this page, draw a simple map of your classroom. Include the walls, doors and windows, and any furniture you wish. Include a compass rose like this one to show which direction is north:

Write one way you know to figure out which direction is north.

_____

_____

_____

_____

_____

©2002 by Evan-Moor Corp.

CASE # 2 Found: A Boot

Present the Ad

Remind students that this is an ad for a found object, and that they should not identify the object until you ask them to. Then follow these steps:

Use Picture Clues

- Ask volunteers to study the picture and say what time of year they think it is and how they can tell. *(Christmas time; stockings hung on mantle, decorated tree, snow falling outside)*

- Ask students if they have enough information to formulate a hypothesis (make a guess) about the found item. Record any ideas they offer.

Use Text Clues

- Have a volunteer read the first sentence aloud and say whether it confirms any assumptions the group has already made.

- Choose a student to read the next two sentences aloud, and invite students to make new hypotheses or revise those already formulated.

- Ask another volunteer to read the rest of the ad and to point out the text that is most helpful in identifying the found object. *(left foot only)*

Found!
Christmas Day in living room fireplace. Tall, black, and shiny. Made of leather. Left foot only with red sock found inside. Stamped with "Made at the North Pole." If this is yours, call Mr. Rudolph at 555-6291.

CASE # 2
What did Mr. Rudolph find?

©2002 by Evan-Moor Corp.   14   Clues to Comprehension, Grades 3-4 • EMC 2721

Present the Solution and Discuss Boots

Invite volunteers to identify the found item *(Santa's boot)* and to describe it using as many adjectives as they can.

Build Vocabulary and Concepts

Lead students in brainstorming descriptive information about Santa Claus. Record their ideas on a character map as shown.

For independent practice, have students complete page 15.

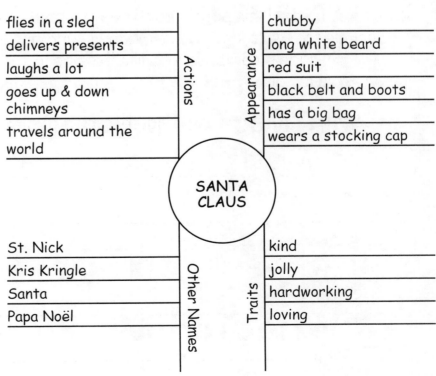

Actions
- flies in a sled
- delivers presents
- laughs a lot
- goes up & down chimneys
- travels around the world

Appearance
- chubby
- long white beard
- red suit
- black belt and boots
- has a big bag
- wears a stocking cap

SANTA CLAUS

Other Names
- St. Nick
- Kris Kringle
- Santa
- Papa Noël

Traits
- kind
- jolly
- hardworking
- loving

Found!

Christmas Day in living room fireplace. Tall, black, and shiny. Made of leather. Left foot only with red sock found inside. Stamped with "Made at the North Pole." If this is yours, call Mr. Rudolph at 555-6291.

CASE #
2

What did Mr. Rudolph find?

Boot It

CASE #
2

1. Where did Mr. Rudolph find the boot?

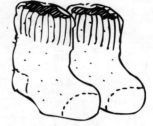

above the mantle   by the tree

in the fireplace   on the roof

2. Choose another name for the **North Pole**.

Alaska   Antarctica   Arctic Circle   Siberia

3. Circle the word that does <u>not</u> belong.

candy cane   smoke   stockings   tinsel

4. Which of the following do <u>not</u> come in pairs?

boots   gloves   socks   ties

5. Use the space below to draw Santa's boots. Show lots of details. Then label each part of the boot. Use words like **fur**, **heel**, **laces**, **leather**, and **sole**.

Found: An American Flag

Present the Ad

Remind students that this is an ad for a found object, and that they should not identify the object until you ask them to. Then follow these steps:

Use Picture Clues

- Invite a volunteer to describe what is shown in the sky *(fireworks)* and to say what the occasion might be. *(Fourth of July, New Year's Eve)*

- Ask students if they have enough information to formulate a hypothesis about the found item. Record any ideas they offer.

Use Text Clues

- Ask a volunteer to read the first sentence aloud and confirm the occasion being celebrated with fireworks. Elicit information from students about the Fourth of July (Independence Day), ensuring that they know this date marks the anniversary of the adoption of the Declaration of Independence in 1776.

- Have a student read the rest of the ad and point out the text that is most helpful in identifying the found object.

Found!
Found in park after Fourth of July parade. Rectangular-shaped cloth. Has 13 stripes and 50 white stars in upper left-hand corner. If you want to wave this at the next parade, call Sam at 555-2486.

CASE #
3
What did Sam find?

©2002 by Evan-Moor Corp.   17   Clues to Comprehension, Grades 3–4 • EMC 2721

Present the Solution and Discuss the American Flag

Invite volunteers to identify the found item *(an American flag)* and to explain the significance of the stars *(the 50 states)* and the stripes *(the original thirteen colonies)*. Encourage students to share what they know about the appropriate ways to display and care for our flag, and to mention other occasions when it is displayed.

Build Vocabulary and Concepts

Use an atlas or another resource to find an example of another nation's flag, or use your state flag. Guide students in comparing that flag with the American flag. Record their comments in a Venn diagram as shown.

For independent practice, have students complete page 18.

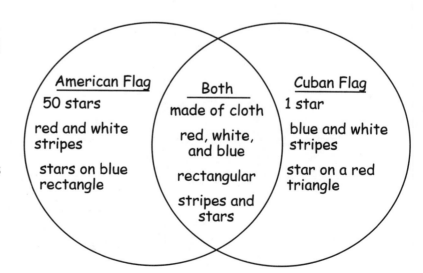

American Flag
50 stars
red and white stripes
stars on blue rectangle

Both
made of cloth
red, white, and blue
rectangular
stripes and stars

Cuban Flag
1 star
blue and white stripes
star on a red triangle

Found!

Found in park after Fourth of July parade. Rectangular-shaped cloth. Has 13 stripes and 50 white stars in upper left-hand corner. If you want to wave this at the next parade, call Sam at 555-2486.

CASE #
3

What did Sam find?

Stars and Stripes

1. Which of the following did <u>not</u> happen on the Fourth of July?

Sam found a flag.   Sam rode a horse.

Sam saw a parade.   Sam walked through the park.

2. Which word is a synonym for **upper**?

left-hand   side   top   under

3. Circle the word that does <u>not</u> belong.

rectangular   square   triangular   wide

4. On which other holiday might you see a parade?

Groundhog Day   Mother's Day   Thanksgiving   Valentine's Day

5. On the back of this page, draw a flag that represents you or your family. Include symbols or pictures that stand for things that are important to you. Then write about what you included on your flag.

_____

_____

_____

_____

_____

Found: A Broom

Present the Ad

Remind students that this is an ad for a found object, and that they should not identify the object until you ask them to. Then follow these steps:

Use Picture Clues

- Invite a volunteer to describe what is shown in the picture, without focusing on the words, and to say whether it shows something real or make-believe.

- Have another student read the parking-lot sign and the signs above the parking spaces, then say what the occasion might be. *(Halloween)*

- Focus students' attention on the empty parking space and encourage them to speculate silently about what might go in that space.

Use Text Clues

- Ask a volunteer to read the first sentence aloud and confirm the occasion. *(Halloween)*

- Have a student read the rest of the ad and point out the text that is most helpful in identifying the found object. *(long wooden handle with straw bottom)*

Found!

October 31st on sidewalk. Long wooden handle with straw bottom. May have been part of a costume. If this was your transportation on Halloween, call Judy at 555-5428.

CASE #
4

What did Judy find?

Present the Solution and Discuss Brooms

Invite volunteers to identify the found item *(a broom)* and to share any information or stories they know about witches and brooms.

Build Vocabulary and Concepts

Point out to students that the characters listed in this ad are all make-believe, or imaginary, and use imaginary means of transportation. Lead students in brainstorming other imaginary characters and their fantastical means of transportation. Record their ideas in a chart as shown.

Imaginary Character	Transportation
witch	broom
Cinderella	pumpkin coach
Mother Goose	flying goose
Superman, Wonder Woman	flying body

For independent practice, have students complete page 21.

Found!

October 31st on sidewalk. Long wooden handle with straw bottom. May have been part of a costume. If this was your transportation on Halloween, call Judy at 555-5428.

CASE #
4

What did Judy find?

A Clean Sweep

1. Which of these characters would <u>not</u> be at the Halloween ball?

Dracula   Frankenstein   the president   Superman

2. Which word could be used in place of **costume**?

disguise   dress   suit   uniform

3. Choose the word that best completes this sentence:

Everyone had a _____ time at the Halloween ball.

| boring | lonely | sad | wild |

4. How many other words can you write that rhyme with **broom**?

_____

_____

5. On the back of this page, draw an imaginary form of transportation that you would like to use. Then describe it in writing.

_____

_____

_____

_____

Found: A Pair of Scissors

Present the Ad

Remind students that this is an ad for a found object, and that they should not identify the object until you ask them to. Then follow these steps:

Use Picture Clues

- Invite a volunteer to describe what the girl and dog are doing. *(carrying groceries after a shopping trip)*

- Ask students if they have enough information to formulate a hypothesis about the found item. Record any ideas they offer.

Use Text Clues

- Ask a volunteer to read the first sentence aloud and confirm that the girl had, in fact, been grocery shopping.

- Have another student read the next two sentences, and encourage speculation about what the object might be.

- Ask another volunteer to read the rest of the ad and point out the text that is most helpful in identifying the found object. *(used to cut)*

Found!
July 20th at Shop Smart Grocery Store. On floor near the dairy section. Pair of sharp, silver blades with handles. Probably used to cut out coupons. Call Sally at 555-2136.

CASE #
5
What did Sally find?

©2002 by Evan-Moor Corp.   23   Clues to Comprehension, Grades 3–4 • EMC 2721

Present the Solution and Discuss Scissors

Invite volunteers to identify the found item *(a pair of scissors)* and to explain what coupons are, and how they are used at the grocery store. *(slips of paper offering a discount or money back on the items shown on the coupon; used to save money)*

Build Vocabulary and Concepts

Invite students to brainstorm other things that can be cut with scissors. Then brainstorm other tools that can be used for cutting and the materials they cut. Record their ideas in a chart as shown.

Cutting Tool	Paper	Cloth	Thread, String	Hair	Meat, Food	Wood
scissors	✓	✓	✓	✓		
knife	✓		✓		✓	
ax						✓
saw						✓

For independent practice, have students complete page 24.

Found!

July 20th at Shop Smart Grocery Store. On floor near the dairy section. Pair of sharp, silver blades with handles. Probably used to cut out coupons. Call Sally at 555-2136.

CASE #
5

What did Sally find?

Cutting Up

1. Choose the word that best completes this sentence:

We saved money at the supermarket by using several _____.

ads	bills	coupons	dollars

2. Which of the following does <u>not</u> have a blade?

an ax   a knife   a spoon   a sword

3. Which word is an antonym for **sharp**?

dull   hard   soft   strong

4. Circle the word that does <u>not</u> belong.

science   scientific   scissors   skin

5. Use the space below to draw a tool with a blade. Add labels that tell what each part is and what it is made of, for example: **silver handle**. Then write a sentence telling how and when this tool is used.

_____

_____

Found: A Dollar Bill

Present the Ad

Remind students that this is an ad for a found object, and that they should not identify the object until you ask them to. Then follow these steps:

Use Picture Clues

- Have a volunteer name the person shown in the picture. *(George Washington)*

- Invite a student to read Washington's words, and be sure everyone is familiar with the reference to the legend about the young George Washington *(who is said to have used these words when confessing to his father that he had cut down their cherry tree).*

- Ask students if they have enough information to formulate a hypothesis about the found item. Record any ideas they offer.

Use Text Clues

- Have a volunteer read the first sentence aloud, and ask students if it provides any helpful information for revising or formulating hypotheses.

- Invite a student to read the next sentence, then encourage speculation about what the object might be.

- Choose a student to read the rest of the ad and to point out the text that is most helpful in identifying the found object.

Found!
August 8th on sidewalk. Rectangular green and white paper item with the number "1" in all four corners. Picture of George Washington on the front, an eagle on the back. Call I.M. Honest at 555-8183 if you can prove it's yours.

CASE # 6
What did I.M. Honest find?

©2002 by Evan-Moor Corp.   26   Clues to Comprehension, Grades 3–4 • EMC 2721

Present the Solution and Discuss Dollar Bills

Invite volunteers to identify the found item *(a dollar bill)* and to share what they know about currency. You may wish to look at bills for $1, $5, $10, and $20. If possible, compare "old" bills to "new," showing the holographic image and discussing the anti-counterfeiting features of the new bills.

Build Vocabulary and Concepts

Point out the name of the person who wrote this ad *(I.M. Honest)* and begin a discussion with students about honesty. Encourage students to find other ways to say what it means to be honest, and to give examples. Record their ideas in a graphic organizer as shown.

For independent practice, have students complete page 27.

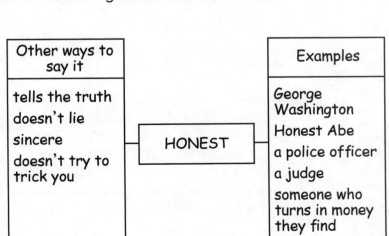

Other ways to say it		Examples
tells the truth doesn't lie sincere doesn't try to trick you	HONEST	George Washington Honest Abe a police officer a judge someone who turns in money they find

Found!

August 8th on sidewalk. Rectangular green and white paper item with the number "1" in all four corners. Picture of George Washington on the front, an eagle on the back. Call I.M. Honest at 555-8183 if you can prove it's yours.

CASE #
6

What did I.M. Honest find?

Honestly!

1. Which of these would <u>not</u> be the right thing to do if you found money?

    try to find whoever lost it   tell your parents

    notify the police   keep it and not tell anybody

2. Which of these could you probably buy with a $1 bill?

    an apple   a book   a piece of gum   a postage stamp

3. Which words mean about the same thing as **prove**?

    give an example   show proof

    trick somebody   write a contract

4. Circle the word that does <u>not</u> belong.

    bank   eagle   president   pyramid

5. If you could design a new $1 bill, what would it look like? Use the back of this page to draw it, then write about something you would like to save money to buy.

_____

_____

_____

_____

_____

Lost!

Lost!
June 1st. Round and white with red stitching. Left on pitcher's mound at Grand Slam Stadium. Has the autographs of all my favorite Major League players. Please call Terry at 555-4321 if you find it.

CASE #
3

What did Terry lose?

Lost!
October 4th on school playground. Round toy on a string. Goes down and comes back up. You can Rock the Cradle, Walk the Dog, and go Around the World with this toy. If found, please call Yolanda at 555-3644.

CASE #
2

What did Yolanda lose?

Lost!
May 22nd, in school cafeteria. Square, plastic food container with handle. Decorated with dinosaurs. Peanut butter and jelly sandwich, bagel chips, grapes, and juice box inside. Please call Jimmy at 555-1491 if you find it.

CASE #
4

What did Jimmy lose?

©2002 by Evan-Moor Corp.

Lost: A Jack-in-the-Box

Present the Ad

Tell students that this is an ad for an object that somebody lost, and that they should not identify the object until you ask them to. Then follow these steps:

Use Picture Clues

- Invite a volunteer to describe the scene in the picture *(a weasel is playing a flute, marching behind a bird dressed as the leader of a parade)* and to speculate about what the lost item might be.

- Have another student read the text on the animal's shirt, then ask students if they have enough information to formulate a hypothesis about the lost item. Record any ideas they offer.

Use Text Clues

- Have a volunteer read the first sentence aloud, and ask students if it provides any helpful information for revising or formulating hypotheses.

- Invite a student to read the next sentence, then encourage speculation about what the object might be.

- Choose a student to read the rest of the ad and to point out the text that is most helpful in identifying the lost object.

Lost!
August 3rd at Flowers Mall. Square-shaped musical toy. Plays "Pop Goes the Weasel" as you turn the handle. If it pops up, please call Jack at 555-6193.

CASE #
1

What did Jack lose?

Present the Solution and Discuss Jack-in-the-Boxes

Invite volunteers to identify the lost item *(a Jack-in-the-Box)* and to share what they know about these fanciful musical toys.

Build Vocabulary and Concepts

Tell students that jack-in-the-boxes are old-fashioned mechanical toys that work with a crank handle. Invite students to brainstorm other old-fashioned, non-electronic toys and list them on one half of a T-chart. Then brainstorm a list of "modern" toys to record on the other half as shown below. Encourage students to compare the two groups, point out similarities and differences, and talk about which toys they prefer and why.

Old-fashioned Toys	Modern Toys
jack-in-the-box	remote-control car
spinning top	Nintendo
yo-yo	Gameboy
jump rope	scooter
jacks	
balls	

For independent practice, have students complete page 31.

Lost!

August 3rd at Flowers Mall. Square-shaped musical toy. Plays "Pop Goes the Weasel" as you turn the handle. If it pops up, please call Jack at 555-6193.

CASE #
1

What did Jack lose?

Pop-Top

1. Which of these is <u>not</u> a musical toy?

a hula-hoop   a jack-in-the-box

a music box   a xylophone

2. Which song might a jack-in-the-box play?

"America, the Beautiful"   "Happy Birthday"

"Jingle Bells"   "Pop Goes the Weasel"

3. What shape was the jack-in-the-box that Jack lost?

a circle   a cube   a cylinder   a pyramid

4. Circle the word that does <u>not</u> belong.

box   handle   lid   remote-control

5. If you could make a jack-in-the-box, what kind of character would pop out when it opened? Draw a picture of it on the back of this page, and then write about it below. Tell what music your jack-in-the-box would play.

_____

_____

_____

_____

Lost: A Yo-Yo

Present the Ad

Remind students that this is an ad for an object that somebody lost, and that they should not identify the object until you ask them to. Then follow these steps:

Use Picture Clues

- Ask a volunteer to describe the scene and to speculate what the fish and dog might be looking at, or what might be on the string looped around the finger.

- Have another student read the text in the speech bubble, then ask students if they have enough information to formulate a hypothesis about the lost item. Record any ideas they offer.

Use Text Clues

- Have a volunteer read the first sentence aloud, and ask students if it provides any helpful information for revising or formulating hypotheses.

- Invite a student to read the next sentence, then encourage speculation about what the object might be.

- Choose a student to read the rest of the ad and to point out the text that is most helpful in identifying the lost object.

IS SOMETHING MISSING?

Lost!

October 4th on school playground. Round toy on a string. Goes down and comes back up. You can Rock the Cradle, Walk the Dog, and go Around the World with this toy. If found, please call Yolanda at 555-3644.

CASE #
2

What did Yolanda lose?

©2002 by Evan-Moor Corp. 33 Clues to Comprehension, Grades 3–4 • EMC 2721

Present the Solution and Discuss Yo-Yos

Invite volunteers to identify the lost item *(a yo-yo)* and to share what they know about these classic toys. Encourage those who know to describe each of the yo-yo tricks mentioned in the ad.

Build Vocabulary and Concepts

Point out the text in the ad that describes the yo-yo as a "round toy." Invite students to brainstorm other round toys and to record them in a graphic organizer as shown.

For independent practice, have students complete page 34.

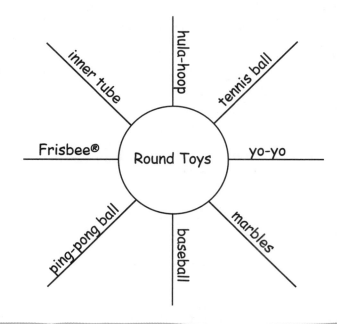

hula-hoop
tennis ball
inner tube
yo-yo
Frisbee®
Round Toys
marbles
baseball
ping-pong ball

Lost!

October 4th on school playground. Round toy on a string. Goes down and comes back up. You can Rock the Cradle, Walk the Dog, and go Around the World with this toy. If found, please call Yolanda at 555-3644.

CASE #
2

What did Yolanda lose?

Up & Down

CASE #
2

1. Which of these materials is <u>not</u> used to make a yo-yo?

metal   paper   plastic   wood

2. Circle the word that is a synonym for **round**.

circular   oval   curved   straight

3. Which of these toys did <u>not</u> exist when your parents were children?

scooters   spinning tops

remote-control robots   yo-yos

4. Circle the word that does <u>not</u> belong.

yarn   string   thread   chain

5. Draw a picture on the back of this page of a trick you would like to learn to do with a yo-yo, or one you already know how to do. Write the name of the trick below and describe how to do it.

_____

_____

_____

_____

_____

Lost: A Baseball

Present the Ad

Remind students that this is an ad for an object that somebody lost, and that they should not identify the object until you ask them to. Then follow these steps:

Use Picture Clues

- Have a volunteer describe the scene and say how the characters in the picture are probably feeling. *(sad)*

- Ask students if they have enough information to formulate a hypothesis about the lost item. Record any ideas they offer.

Use Text Clues

- Have a volunteer read the first two sentences aloud, and ask students if they provide any helpful information for revising or formulating hypotheses.

- Invite a student to read the next two sentences and to point out the text that is most helpful in identifying the lost object.

- Choose a student to read the rest of the ad and to point out "Terry" in the picture.

Lost!
June 1st. Round and white with red stitching. Left on pitcher's mound at Grand Slam Stadium. Has the autographs of all my favorite Major League players. Please call Terry at 555-4321 if you find it.

CASE #
3

What did Terry lose?

©2002 by Evan-Moor Corp.   36   Clues to Comprehension, Grades 3–4 • EMC 2721

Present the Solution and Discuss Baseballs

Invite volunteers to identify the lost item *(a baseball)* and to share what they know about baseballs, what they are made of, and how they are used.

Build Vocabulary and Concepts

Point out the bat, gloves, and face mask in the picture, and tell students that there is other equipment besides a ball that is used to play the game of baseball. Invite students to brainstorm other ball games, and to categorize them according to whether they require the use of additional equipment. Record their ideas in a T-chart as shown.

Ball Games Without Equipment	Ball Games with Equipment
dodgeball	tennis (racquet, net)
4-square	volleyball (net)
2-square	basketball (hoops)
catch	football (masks, pads)
soccer	bowling (pins)
handball	

For independent practice, have students complete page 37.

Lost!

June 1st. Round and white with red stitching. Left on pitcher's mound at Grand Slam Stadium. Has the autographs of all my favorite Major League players. Please call Terry at 555-4321 if you find it.

CASE #
3

What did Terry lose?

Play Ball!

1. Circle two meanings of the word **pitcher**.

a small box for jewelry   a dog trained to fetch

a player on a baseball team   a container to hold and pour liquid

2. Which word means about the same thing as **mound**?

ground   hill   mountain   pound

3. Choose the best word to complete this sentence:

I passed the player my fancy pen so he could give me his _____.

| autograph | bat | cap | paper |

4. Circle the word that does <u>not</u> belong.

catcher   goalie   pitcher   outfielder

5. Whose autograph would you like to have? On the back of this page, draw a
picture of yourself asking that person for an autograph. Use the lines below to
write what you would say to ask the person for an autograph. Don't forget to use
quotation marks.

_____

_____

_____

_____

Lost: A Lunch Box

Present the Ad

Remind students that this is an ad for an object that somebody lost, and that they should not identify the object until you ask them to. Then follow these steps:

Use Picture Clues

- Invite a volunteer to name the items on the table in front of the boy *(grapes, a sandwich, juice, bagel chips)* and tell how the boy looks. *(sad)*

- Have another student describe what is happening behind the boy *(food is flying through the air; other children are getting hit by the food)* and then guess where this scene is set. *(in a school cafeteria)*

- Ask students if they have enough information to formulate a hypothesis about the lost item. Record any ideas they offer.

Use Text Clues

- Have a volunteer read the first sentence and confirm the setting.

- Ask another student to read the next sentence, and ask if it provides any helpful information for revising or formulating hypotheses.

- Invite a student to read the rest of the ad and to point out the text that is most helpful in identifying the lost object.

Lost!
May 22nd, in school cafeteria. Square, plastic food container with handle. Decorated with dinosaurs. Peanut butter and jelly sandwich, bagel chips, grapes, and juice box inside. Please call Jimmy at 555-1491 if you find it.

CASE #
4
What did Jimmy lose?

©2002 by Evan-Moor Corp.   3/4   Clues to Comprehension, Grades 3-4 • EMC 2721

Present the Solution and Discuss Lunch Boxes

Invite volunteers to identify the lost item *(a lunch box)* and to share information about their lunch boxes or other items used to carry food to school.

Build Vocabulary and Concepts

Tell students that a healthy, balanced meal includes protein, fruit and vegetables, and grains. Encourage students to brainstorm healthy foods that they could bring for lunch, and categorize them on a food pyramid as shown.

For independent practice, have students complete page 40.

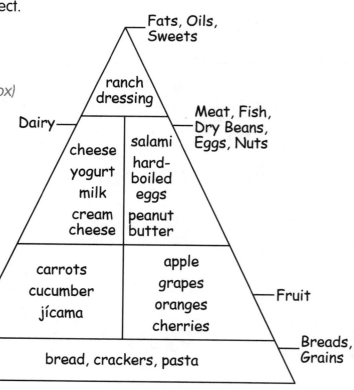

Fats, Oils, Sweets

ranch dressing

Dairy

Meat, Fish, Dry Beans, Eggs, Nuts

cheese yogurt milk cream cheese

salami hard-boiled eggs peanut butter

Vegetables

carrots cucumber jícama

apple grapes oranges cherries

Fruit

bread, crackers, pasta

Breads, Grains

Lost!

May 22nd, in school cafeteria. Square, plastic food container with handle. Decorated with dinosaurs. Peanut butter and jelly sandwich, bagel chips, grapes, and juice box inside. Please call Jimmy at 555-1491 if you find it.

CASE #
4

What did Jimmy lose?

Name _____

Lunch Bunch

1. Which word does <u>not</u> describe Jimmy's lunch box?

    full   metal   plastic   square

2. Which of the following is a synonym for **cafeteria**?

    classroom   dining hall   kitchen   library

3. Which food is <u>not</u> part of a healthy meal?

    carrots   milk   cupcakes   cheese sandwich

4. Circle the word that does <u>not</u> belong.

    lunch box   paper bag   suitcase   thermos

5. On the back of this page, draw a picture of a healthy, balanced lunch that you would like to eat. Use the lines below to write your healthy lunch menu.

_____

_____

_____

_____

_____

_____

CASE # 5 Lost: A Kite

Present the Ad

Remind students that this is an ad for an object that somebody lost, and that they should not identify the object until you ask them to. Then follow these steps:

Use Picture Clues

- Invite a volunteer to describe the scene in the picture.
  (A powerful wind is blowing.)

- Have another student read the text in the speech bubble, then encourage students to hypothesize about the lost item.

Use Text Clues

- Have a volunteer read the first sentence, and ask what season it is *(spring)* and whether windy weather conditions are common in the spring. *(yes)* Invite students to formulate or revise hypotheses.

- Ask another student to read the second sentence, and ask whether this confirms any of the hypotheses.

- Choose a student to read the rest of the ad and to point out the text that is most helpful in identifying the lost object.

WHERE'S MY FRIEND WHO LIKES TO FLY?

Lost!
Saturday, April 12th, while playing in the field near U.R. Bright School. Made of cloth with wooden frame. Diamond-shaped with long tail. String broke. Last seen flying over school building. If found, call Steve at 555-3378.

CASE # 5
What did Steve lose?

©2002 by Evan-Moor Corp.   42   Clues to Comprehension, Grades 3-4 • EMC 2721

Present the Solution and Discuss Kites

Invite volunteers to identify the lost item *(a kite)* and to share any experiences they have had with kites.

Build Vocabulary and Concepts

Lead students in brainstorming words that describe kites. Record their ideas on a graphic organizer as shown.

For independent practice, have students complete page 43.

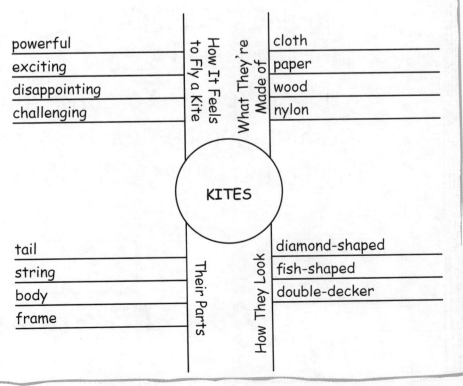

How It Feels to Fly a Kite:
- powerful
- exciting
- disappointing
- challenging

What They're Made of:
- cloth
- paper
- wood
- nylon

KITES

Their Parts:
- tail
- string
- body
- frame

How They Look:
- diamond-shaped
- fish-shaped
- double-decker

Lost!

Saturday, April 12th, while playing in the field near U.R. Bright School. Made of cloth with wooden frame. Diamond-shaped with long tail. String broke. Last seen flying over school building. If found, call Steve at 555-3378.

CASE #
5

What did Steve lose?

©2002 by Evan-Moor Corp.

Clues to Comprehension, Grades 3–4 • EMC 2721

Up, Up, and Away

1. How might Steve have lost his kite?

It crashed into the ocean.   It got caught in a tree.

The frame broke.   The string broke.

2. Which word is an antonym for **long**?

large   short   strong   tall

3. Choose the word that <u>cannot</u> complete this sentence:

You need lots of _____ to fly a kite.

cloth	space	string	wind

4. Circle the word that does <u>not</u> belong.

Frisbee®   glider   kite   skis

5. On the back of this page, draw a picture of a kite that you would like to fly. Use the lines below to write about where you would go to fly it.

_____

_____

_____

_____

Present the Ad

Remind students that this is an ad for an object that somebody lost, and that they should not identify the object until you ask them to. Then follow these steps:

Use Picture Clues

- Invite a volunteer to describe what the dog is doing. *(leaping into the air)*

- Ask students if they have enough information to hypothesize about the lost item. Record any ideas they offer.

Use Text Clues

- Have a volunteer read the first two sentences, and ask whether they provide any additional information about the lost item.

- Ask another student to read the third sentence, and encourage speculation about what the lost item might be.

- Have another student read the rest of the ad and point out the text that is most helpful in identifying the lost object.

Lost!
July 10th. Left on Sunshine Beach. Thin, round plastic disk with white and black stripes. Can be thrown and caught. Please call Susan at 555-8541.

CASE #
6

What did Susan lose?

©2002 by Evan-Moor Corp.   45   Clues to Comprehension, Grades 3–4 • EMC 2721

Present the Solution and Discuss Frisbees®

Invite volunteers to identify the lost item *(a Frisbee®)* and to share what they know about Frisbees®.

Build Vocabulary and Concepts

Tell students that people often imagine that alien spacecraft from outer space look like flying saucers, or Frisbees®. Have students compare Frisbees® and flying saucers, and record their comments in a Venn diagram as shown.

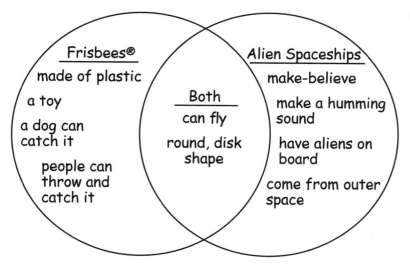

Frisbees®
made of plastic
a toy
a dog can catch it
people can throw and catch it

Both
can fly
round, disk shape

Alien Spaceships
make-believe
make a humming sound
have aliens on board
come from outer space

For independent practice, have students complete page 46.

Lost!

July 10th. Left on Sunshine Beach. Thin, round plastic disk with white and black stripes. Can be thrown and caught. Please call Susan at 555-8541.

CASE #
6

What did Susan lose?

©2002 by Evan-Moor Corp.

Clues to Comprehension, Grades 3–4 • EMC 2721

Flying Saucers

1. Where did Susan lose her Frisbee®?

at school   at the park   on the beach   on the playground

2. How many words can you write that rhyme with **caught**?

_____

_____

3. Which word is <u>not</u> a synonym for **thin**?

narrow   skinny   slender   thick

4. Circle the word that does <u>not</u> belong.

frogs   sand   water   waves

5. On the back of this page, draw a picture of an alien spacecraft and the type of alien that is on board. Use the lines below to write about where this spacecraft came from and what the aliens are like.

_____

_____

_____

_____

_____

Lost: Ten Sheep

Present the Ad

Remind students that this is an ad for something that somebody lost, and that they should not identify the lost item until you ask them to. Then follow these steps:

Use Picture Clues

Lost!
May 17th from Peep's Meadow. Ten farm animals. All white and woolly. I can't tell where to find them. Please help me get them baaack. Call Bo at 555-7943.

CASE #
7
What did Bo lose?

- Invite a volunteer to describe the scene *(a girl holding a shepherd's crook is crying; a dog is next to her; there are fields in the countryside and a house)* and to say who the little girl might be. *(a shepherd; Little Bo Peep)*

- Ask students if they have enough information to hypothesize about the lost item. Record any ideas they offer.

Use Text Clues

- Have a volunteer read the first sentence, and ask whether it gives any additional information about the girl's identity.

- Ask another student to read the second sentence, and encourage speculation about what animals might be lost.

- Have another student read the rest of the ad and point out the text that is most helpful in identifying the lost object.

Present the Solution and Discuss Sheep

Invite volunteers to identify the lost item *(10 sheep)* and to share what they know about sheep. Be sure all students recognize the reference to the nursery rhyme about Little Bo Peep *(Little Bo Peep has lost her sheep/and can't tell where to find them./Leave them alone and they will come home,/wagging their tails behind them.)* and understand that "back" is written as "baaack" to imitate the sound made by sheep.

Build Vocabulary and Concepts

Lead students in brainstorming about sheep—their appearance; their products; and the various names for adult, male, female, and baby sheep. Record students' comments in a graphic organizer as shown.

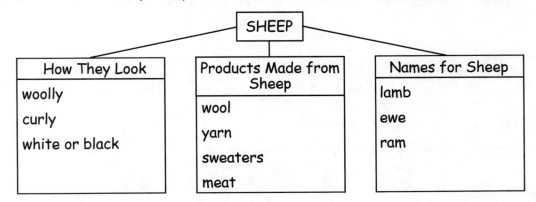

How They Look	Products Made from Sheep	Names for Sheep
woolly	wool	lamb
curly	yarn	ewe
white or black	sweaters	ram
	meat	

For independent practice, have students complete page 49.

Lost!

May 17th from Peep's Meadow. Ten farm animals. All white and woolly. I can't tell where to find them. Please help me get them baaack. Call Bo at 555-7943.

CASE #
7

What did Bo lose?

Counting Sheep

1. Choose the word or words that <u>cannot</u> complete this sentence:

Little Bo Peep is _____.

| a shepherd | crying | inside the barn | upset |

2. How many words can you write that rhyme with **wool**?

_____

_____

3. Which word is a synonym for **woolly**?

cozy   fuzzy   scratchy   thick

4. Circle the word that does <u>not</u> belong.

mittens   socks   shoes   sweater

5. On the back of this page, draw a picture to show where Little Bo Peep's sheep were. Use the lines below to tell how she found them again.

_____

_____

_____

_____

_____

Present the Ad

Remind students that this is an ad for something that somebody lost, and that they should not identify the lost item until you ask them to. Then follow these steps:

Use Picture Clues

• Invite a volunteer to describe the scene and to speculate about who might live in the house.

• Have another student read the sign on the door and indicate whether it offers additional information to help formulate a hypothesis. Record any ideas offered.

Use Text Clues

• Have a volunteer read the first sentence, and encourage speculation about what sort of winter clothing comes in pairs. *(boots, socks, mittens, etc.)*

• Ask another student to read the second sentence, and have students revise or formulate hypotheses about the lost items.

• Have another student read the rest of the ad and point out the text that is most helpful in identifying the lost object and the identity of Kitty.

Lost!
Winter clothing, three pairs. White, warm, woolen, and worn on hands. We were naughty and left them outside. Nobody's purrfect! Now our mother won't let us have any pie until they're found. Please hurry! Call Kitty at 555-MEOW.

CASE #
8
What did Kitty lose?

Present the Solution and Discuss Mittens

Invite volunteers to identify the lost item *(mittens)*, and make sure that all students recognize the reference to the nursery rhyme about the three little kittens. *(The three little kittens,/they lost their mittens, and they began to cry,/"Oh, Mother, dear,/we sadly fear/our mittens we have lost."/"What! Lost your mittens!/You naughty kittens!/Then you shall have no pie.")* Review the rhyme, then have students point out the references to it in the ad.

Build Vocabulary and Concepts

Remind students that mittens have a separate space for the thumb, but all the fingers are together in one section. Ask them to compare mittens to gloves using as much detail as possible. Record their ideas in a Venn diagram as shown.

For independent practice, have students complete page 52.

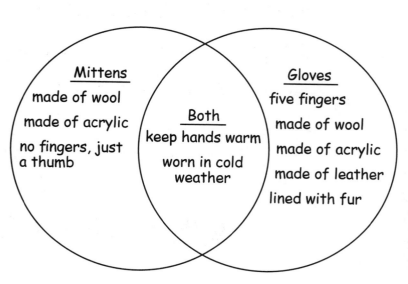

Mittens
made of wool
made of acrylic
no fingers, just a thumb

Both
keep hands warm
worn in cold weather

Gloves
five fingers
made of wool
made of acrylic
made of leather
lined with fur

Lost!

Winter clothing, three pairs. White, warm, woolen, and worn on hands. We were naughty and left them outside. Nobody's purrfect! Now our mother won't let us have any pie until they're found. Please hurry! Call Kitty at 555-MEOW.

CASE #
8

What did Kitty lose?

©2002 by Evan-Moor Corp.

Hands Up

1. Where did the three little kittens leave their mittens?

at school   in the kitchen

outside the house   under their beds

2. How many words can you write that rhyme with **pie**?

_____

_____

3. Which word is an antonym for **naughty**?

bad   good   nasty   terrific

4. Circle the word that does <u>not</u> belong.

gloves   mittens   necklace   rings

5. What kind of pie would you like if you could have a slice right now? Draw a picture of it on the back of this page and use the lines below to describe it.

_____

_____

_____

_____

_____

Lost: A Ruler

Present the Ad

Remind students that this is an ad for something that somebody lost, and that they should not identify the lost item until you ask them to. Then follow these steps:

Use Picture Clues

Lost!
Last week at Young School. Wooden school supply item used to measure length and draw straight lines. 12 inches long. Last seen by blue bulletin board in main hallway. If found, please return it to me. I don't want to buy a new one. Call Brad at 555-6943.

CASE 9
What did Brad lose?

©2002 by Evan-Moor Corp. 54 Clues to Comprehension, Grades 3-4 • EMC 2721

- Invite a volunteer to name the objects on the table with the cat *(an eraser, a pencil, crayons, scissors, a stapler, a paper clip, paper)* and to speculate about where they might be found. *(at school; in a homework area at home)*

- Ask students if they have enough information to hypothesize about the lost item. Record any ideas they offer.

Use Text Clues

- Invite a volunteer to read the first sentence and verify the setting. *(at school)*

- Have another student read the second sentence, and ask if there is enough information to identify the lost item.

- Choose a student to read the rest of the ad and point out the text that is most helpful in identifying the lost object.

Present the Solution and Discuss Rulers

Invite volunteers to identify the lost item *(a ruler)* and to share what they know about rulers and measuring.

Build Vocabulary and Concepts

Lead students in brainstorming about tools used to measure and how they are used. Record their ideas in a chart as shown.

Tools for Measuring	What They Measure
ruler	length of small things
yardstick	length of longer things
measuring tape	really long lengths (a room)
measuring spoons	liquids and powders for cooking
measuring cups	liquids and other foods for cooking
scale	weight of objects

For independent practice, have students complete page 55.

Lost!

Last week at Young School. Wooden school
supply item used to measure length and
draw straight lines. 12 inches long. Last seen
by blue bulletin board in main hallway. If
found, please return it to me. I don't want to
buy a new one. Call Brad at 555-6943.

CASE #
9

What did Brad lose?

You Rule!

1. What will happen if Brad doesn't find his ruler?

He'll have to buy a new one.   He'll have to quit school.

He'll be sent to talk with the principal.   He'll get extra homework.

2. How many words can you write that rhyme with **rule**?

_____

_____

3. What is another meaning of **ruler**?

someone who breaks rules   someone who follows rules

the owner of a company   the leader of a country

4. Circle the word that does <u>not</u> belong.

scale   pole   teaspoon   yardstick

5. On the back of this page, trace your foot or hand. Use a ruler to measure it. Use these lines to write down how long it is.

_____

_____

_____

_____

_____

Help Wanted!

Help Wanted!
10, 9, 8...Begin your countdown to an exciting new job with Space, Inc. 7, 6, 5...You'll be flying high above Earth in one of our rockets. 4, 3, 2...Travel to the Moon, float in space, and study distant planets. 1...Blast off to adventure! Call 555-STAR for an interview.

CASE # 1

Who would answer this ad?

Help Wanted!
It's an emergency! We need to hire a responsible person to drive sick people to the hospital in our speedy vehicle. Must have a safe driving record and know how to use a siren. For an interview, call 555-9245.

CASE # 2

Who would answer this ad?

Help Wanted!
It's a dirty job, but someone has to do it! Could that someone be you? You can help keep your town's streets looking neat and clean. Must be strong enough to lift heavy bags and empty trash cans into large truck. Uniform provided. Call 555-3394.

CASE # 5

Who would answer this ad?

©2002 by Evan-Moor Corp.

Clues to Comprehension, Grades 3–4 • EMC 2721

Help Wanted: An Astronaut

Present the Ad

Tell students that this is a "help wanted" ad, encouraging someone to apply for a job.
Ask students not to identify the type of position in the ad until you ask them to. Then follow these steps:

Use Picture Clues

• Invite a volunteer to describe this picture. *(a spaceship flying over Earth)*

• Ask students whether they have enough information to formulate a hypothesis about the type of job being advertised. Record any ideas they offer.

Use Text Clues

• Have a volunteer read the first sentence, and encourage speculation about what sort of position is being advertised.

• Ask another student to read the rest of the ad and point out the text that is most helpful in identifying the type of job being advertised.

Help Wanted!
10, 9, 8...Begin your countdown to an exciting new job with Space, Inc. 7, 6, 5...You'll be flying high above Earth in one of our rockets. 4, 3, 2...Travel to the Moon, float in space, and study distant planets. 1...Blast off to adventure! Call 555-STAR for an interview.

CASE # 1
Who would answer this ad?

©2002 by Evan-Moor Corp. 58 Clues to Comprehension, Grades 3–4 • EMC 2721

Present the Solution and Discuss Astronauts

Invite volunteers to identify the type of professional that could answer this ad *(an astronaut)* and to share what they know about astronauts.

Build Vocabulary and Concepts

Lead students in brainstorming about astronauts and the type of knowledge needed for this highly technical profession. Record students' ideas in a web as shown.

For independent practice, have students complete page 59.

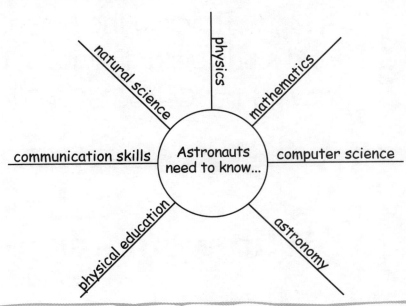

natural science • physics • mathematics • computer science • astronomy • physical education • communication skills

Astronauts need to know...

Help Wanted!

10, 9, 8...Begin your countdown to an exciting new job with Space, Inc. 7, 6, 5...You'll be flying high above Earth in one of our rockets. 4, 3, 2...Travel to the Moon, float in space, and study distant planets. 1...Blast off to adventure! Call 555-STAR for an interview.

CASE #
1

Who would answer this ad?

Blast Off!

1. Which of these is something an astronaut has <u>not</u> done yet?

    float in space   study planets   talk with aliens   visit the Moon

2. Choose an antonym for the word **float**.

    boast   fall   sink   weigh

3. Circle the word that does <u>not</u> belong.

    glider   rocket   space shuttle   space station

4. Choose the best word to complete this sentence:

    The spacecraft splashed down after _____ Earth for one week.

completing	orbiting	studying	visiting

5. If you could be an astronaut, what sort of adventure would you like to have? Draw a picture of it on the back of this page. Use these lines to write about what you would do.

_____

_____

_____

_____

Present the Ad

Remind students that this is a "help wanted" ad, and that they should not identify the type of worker being sought until you ask them to. Then follow these steps:

Use Picture Clues

- Invite a volunteer to describe this scene. *(Two of the King's men are transporting Humpty Dumpty on a stretcher.)*

- Ask students if they have enough information to formulate a hypothesis about the type of worker sought in this ad. Record any ideas they offer.

Use Text Clues

- Ask a volunteer to read the first sentence and speculate about what kind of worker is needed.

- Have another student read the second sentence, and encourage students to hypothesize about this job.

- Ask another student to read the rest of the ad and point out the text that is most helpful in identifying the type of worker sought.

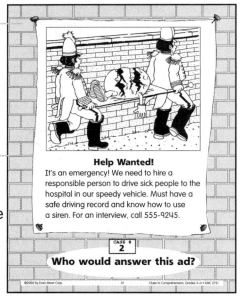

Help Wanted!
It's an emergency! We need to hire a responsible person to drive sick people to the hospital in our speedy vehicle. Must have a safe driving record and know how to use a siren. For an interview, call 555-9245.

CASE #
2
Who would answer this ad?

Present the Solution and Discuss Ambulance Drivers

Invite volunteers to identify the type of worker being sought in this ad *(an ambulance driver)*, and to talk about why an ambulance driver must be responsible and have a safe driving record.

Build Vocabulary and Concepts

Tell students that ambulance drivers are emergency-response workers. Encourage them to brainstorm other emergency-response workers, and record their ideas in a graphic organizer as shown.

For independent practice, have students complete page 62.

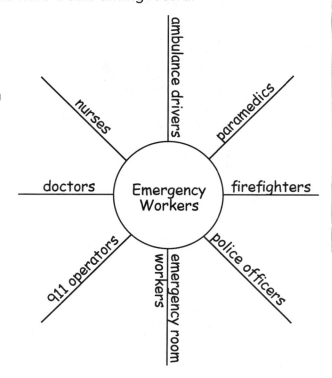

Emergency!

1. Which of the following is <u>not</u> an emergency?

a building is burning   a car just crashed

someone is choking   someone is crying

2. Choose an antonym for **speedy**.

fast   needy   slow   swift

3. Circle the word that does <u>not</u> belong.

ambulance   hose   bandage   stretcher

4. Choose the best words to complete this sentence:

Someone who is responsible is _____ .

a person who is careless	a person you can count on
always afraid to try new things	always late for everything

5. On the back of this page, draw a picture of an emergency in which you would need to call an ambulance. Use these lines to explain what happened.

_____

_____

_____

_____

Present the Ad

Remind students that this is a "help wanted" ad, and that they should not identify the type of worker being sought until you ask them to. Then follow these steps:

Use Picture Clues

- Ask a volunteer to identify the creature in the picture *(a "bookworm")* and to explain what helped him or her reach that conclusion.

- Invite another student to read the text in the speech bubble and to say whether there is now enough information to formulate a hypothesis about the type of worker sought in this ad. Record any suggestions offered.

Use Text Clues

- Ask a volunteer to read the first two sentences aloud, confirm that the creature is a "bookworm," and explain what a bookworm is. *(someone who loves books)*

- Have another student read the next two sentences and speculate about the setting described in this ad. *(a library)*

- Invite a student to read the rest of the ad and point out the humorous text embedded in the ad. *(follow library rules by the book; Reed Library)* You may need to introduce the term "pun" as "a play on words" or "using words in a humorous way."

> **Maybe I could get a job here!**
>
> **Help Wanted!**
> Do you love to read? Are you a bookworm? Can you say, "Shhh!" when there's too much noise? We need you to work in our reference section. You'll help students locate information and follow library rules by the book. Call Reed Library at 555-2461 if interested.
>
> CASE # 3
> **Who would answer this ad?**
>
> ©2002 by Evan-Moor Corp.   64   Clues to Comprehension, Grades 3–4 • EMC 2721

Present the Solution and Discuss Librarians

Invite volunteers to identify the type of worker being sought in this ad *(a librarian)* and to talk about what a librarian does. Be sure that students understand what a "reference section" is.

Build Vocabulary and Concepts

Remind students that librarians need to know how to categorize books. Begin a graphic organizer with the headings shown below, and encourage students to provide examples for each type of book.

For independent practice, have students complete page 65.

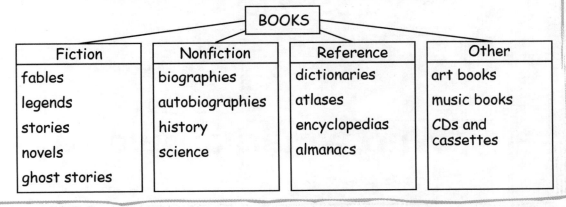

BOOKS

Fiction	Nonfiction	Reference	Other
fables	biographies	dictionaries	art books
legends	autobiographies	atlases	music books
stories	history	encyclopedias	CDs and cassettes
novels	science	almanacs	
ghost stories			

Maybe I could get a job here!

Help Wanted!

Do you love to read? Are you a bookworm? Can you say, "Shhh!" when there's too much noise? We need you to work in our reference section. You'll help students locate information and follow library rules by the book. Call Reed Library at 555-2461 if interested.

CASE #
3

Who would answer this ad?

Check It Out

1. Which of the following is <u>not</u> part of a librarian's job?

    helping people buy books   helping people find reference materials

    helping people search on the Internet   helping to keep the library quiet

2. Circle a synonym for **locate**.

    direct   find   lose   research

3. Circle the word that does <u>not</u> belong.

    atlas   dictionary   encyclopedia   novel

4. Circle the word or words a librarian would probably <u>not</u> use in the library.

    "Hush!"   "Quiet, please."   "Shhh."   "Shut up!"

5. On the back of this page, draw a picture of one of your favorite characters from a book you have read. Use the lines below to write the title of the book and the character's name.

_____

_____

_____

_____

_____

©2002 by Evan-Moor Corp.

Clues to Comprehension, Grades 3–4 • EMC 2721

Present the Ad

Remind students that this is a "help wanted" ad, and that they should not identify the type of worker being sought until you ask them to. Then follow these steps:

Use Picture Clues

- Ask a volunteer to describe the scene in the picture *(children waiting at a school bus stop)* and to point out the picture clues that support that conclusion.

- Invite another student to read the text on the sign and confirm the setting.

- Ask students whether they have enough information to formulate a hypothesis about the type of worker sought in this ad. Record any suggestions offered.

Use Text Clues

- Ask a volunteer to read the first sentence aloud and confirm or revise hypotheses.

- Have another student read the rest of the ad and point out the text that provides the best clues about the type of worker sought in this ad.

Help Wanted!
School district needs person to drive large yellow vehicle five days a week from September until June. Must be available for field trips. Responsible for getting student passengers to school and home safely. Call 555-6321.

CASE #
4
Who would answer this ad?

©2002 by Evan-Moor Corp.   67   Clues to Comprehension, Grades 3–4 • EMC 2721

Present the Solution and Discuss School Bus Drivers

Invite volunteers to identify the type of worker being sought in this ad *(a school bus driver)* and to talk about school bus drivers and their work.

Build Vocabulary and Concepts

Lead students in discussing desirable qualities for a school bus driver and comparing them to those needed by a city bus driver. Record their comments in a Venn diagram as shown.

For independent practice, have students complete page 68.

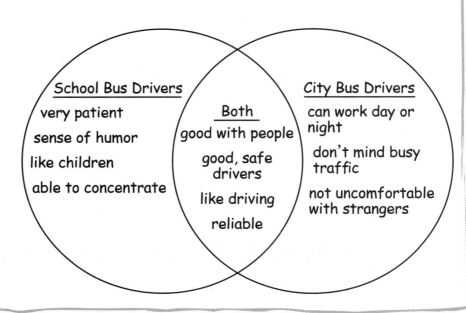

School Bus Drivers
very patient
sense of humor
like children
able to concentrate

Both
good with people
good, safe drivers
like driving
reliable

City Bus Drivers
can work day or night
don't mind busy traffic
not uncomfortable with strangers

Help Wanted!

School district needs person to drive large yellow vehicle five days a week from September until June. Must be available for field trips. Responsible for getting student passengers to school and home safely. Call 555-6321.

CASE #
4

Who would answer this ad?

©2002 by Evan-Moor Corp.

Clues to Comprehension, Grades 3–4 • EMC 2721

Name ______________________________

Bus Stop

CASE # 4

1. Choose the word that <u>cannot</u> complete this sentence:

A bus driver needs to be very ______________ .

careful	patient	reliable	sleepy

2. Which prefix can you add to **responsible** to make its antonym?

dis- ir- sub- un-

3. Circle the word that does <u>not</u> belong.

bus van truck submarine

4. Write as many synonyms as you can for **large**.

____

____

5. If you could drive any vehicle, what would it be? Draw a picture of it on the back of this page. Use these lines to describe it.

____

____

____

____

____

©2002 by Evan-Moor Corp.

Present the Ad

Remind students that this is a "help wanted" ad, and that they should not identify the type of worker being sought until you ask them to. Then follow these steps:

Use Picture Clues

- Invite a volunteer to describe the scene. *(overflowing garbage cans and scavengers—raccoon, crow, and cats)*

- Ask students whether they have enough information to formulate a hypothesis about the type of worker sought in this ad. Record any suggestions offered.

Use Text Clues

- Ask a volunteer to read the first two sentences aloud and speculate about what kind of worker this ad is seeking.

- Have another student read the rest of the ad and point out the text that provides the best clues about the type of worker sought in this ad.

Help Wanted!
It's a dirty job, but someone has to do it! Could that someone be you? You can help keep your town's streets looking neat and clean. Must be strong enough to lift heavy bags and empty trash cans into large truck. Uniform provided. Call 555-3394.

CASE #
5
Who would answer this ad?

©2002 by Evan-Moor Corp.   70   Clues to Comprehension, Grades 3–4 • EMC 2721

Present the Solution and Discuss
Sanitation Workers

Invite volunteers to identify the type of worker being sought in this ad *(a sanitation worker)* and to talk about the importance of their work. This would also be a good opportunity to talk about the benefits of recycling, and to review recycling guidelines for your area.

Build Vocabulary and Concepts

Students will have no problem brainstorming the negative aspects of a sanitation worker's job. Encourage them to stretch their thinking by also listing some of the positive aspects. Record their comments in a T-chart as shown.

For independent practice, have students complete page 71.

SANITATION WORKERS	
+ Positive Things	**—** Negative Things
help keep neighborhoods clean	have to be around smelly garbage
get to meet lots of people	have to maneuver a huge truck
get to drive a giant truck	get chased by mean dogs
get to ride on the back of the truck	have to do lots of heavy lifting
get to build great muscles	

Help Wanted!

It's a dirty job, but someone has to do it!
Could that someone be you? You can help
keep your town's streets looking neat and
clean. Must be strong enough to lift heavy
bags and empty trash cans into large truck.
Uniform provided. Call 555-3394.

CASE #
5

Who would answer this ad?

Name ____________________

Can It!

CASE # 5

1. Circle the word that <u>cannot</u> be used to complete this sentence:

Sanitation workers do __________ work.

dirty	garden	important	smelly

2. Which prefix can you add to **clean** to make its antonym?

dis- re- sub- un-

3. Circle the word that does <u>not</u> belong.

bag bin tray can

4. How many words can you write that rhyme with **clean**?

____

____

5. How many things in your lunch can you recycle? How many go in the trash? List them in two columns on these lines.

____

____

____

____

____

©2002 by Evan-Moor Corp.

Help Wanted: An Actor or Actress

Present the Ad

Remind students that this is a "help wanted" ad, and that they should not identify the type of worker being sought until you ask them to. Then follow these steps:

Use Picture Clues

- Ask a volunteer to describe the scene. *(a theater in a busy city)*

- Have a student read the text on the marquee to confirm the setting.

- Ask students whether they have enough information to formulate a hypothesis about the type of worker sought in this ad. Record any suggestions offered.

Use Text Clues

- Ask a volunteer to read the first sentence aloud and speculate about what kind of worker this ad is seeking.

- Have another student read the rest of the ad and point out the text that provides the best clues about the type of worker sought in this ad.

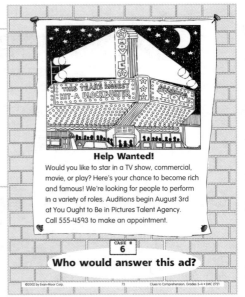

Help Wanted!

Would you like to star in a TV show, commercial, movie, or play? Here's your chance to become rich and famous! We're looking for people to perform in a variety of roles. Auditions begin August 3rd at You Ought to Be in Pictures Talent Agency. Call 555-4593 to make an appointment.

CASE #
6

Who would answer this ad?

©2002 by Evan-Moor Corp. 73 Clues to Comprehension, Grades 3–4 • EMC 2721

Present the Solution and Discuss Actors and Actresses

Invite volunteers to identify the type of worker being sought in this ad *(an actor or actress)*. Make sure that all students understand what an "audition" is and how a talent agency works.

Build Vocabulary and Concepts

Begin a discussion about the types of skills needed by an actor or actress. Record comments in a graphic organizer as shown.

For independent practice, have students complete page 74.

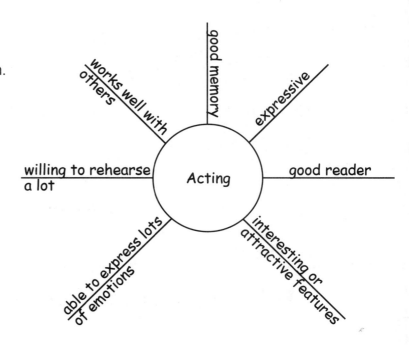

works well with others

good memory

expressive

willing to rehearse a lot

Acting

good reader

able to express lots of emotions

interesting or attractive features

Help Wanted!

Would you like to star in a TV show, commercial, movie, or play? Here's your chance to become rich and famous! We're looking for people to perform in a variety of roles. Auditions begin August 3rd at You Ought to Be in Pictures Talent Agency. Call 555-4593 to make an appointment.

CASE #
6

Who would answer this ad?

Curtain Call

1. Choose the best word or words to complete this sentence:

When you audition, you _____ for a role.

dress up	pay	practice	try out

2. Which word is a synonym for **talent**?

ability   grace   information   knowledge

3. Circle the word that does <u>not</u> belong.

movie   book   opera   play

4. How many words can you write that rhyme with **ought**?

_____

_____

5. If you could be a famous actor or actress, would you prefer to perform in plays, movies, or on television? On the back of this page, draw a picture of yourself performing. Use these lines to write about where you are and what you are performing.

_____

_____

_____

_____

CASE # 7 — Help Wanted: A Firefighter

Present the Ad

Remind students that this is a "help wanted" ad, and that they should not identify the type of worker being sought until you ask them to. Then follow these steps:

Use Picture Clues

- Ask a volunteer to name the animal and the other items in the picture. *(a dalmatian holding a note; boots, a pole)* Encourage speculation about the type of worker sought in this ad. Record any suggestions offered.

- Have a student read the text on the note and revise or formulate new hypotheses.

Use Text Clues

- Ask a volunteer to read the first sentence aloud and note which of the workers already suggested by students are community helpers.

- Have another student read the rest of the ad and point out the text that provides the best clues about the type of worker sought in this ad.

~Help Wanted~
Someone I can sit beside on the truck and who will feed me treats!

Help Wanted!
Help your community! Engine Company No. 4 is looking for brave, strong people who can climb a ladder, drive a large vehicle, use a hose, get dressed quickly, and slide down a pole. Uniform, including helmet and boots, will be provided. Apply in person April 19th at 1625 Dalmatian Drive.

CASE # 7

Who would answer this ad?

©2002 by Evan-Moor Corp.   76   Clues to Comprehension, Grades 3–4 • EMC 2721

Present the Solution and Discuss Firefighters

Invite volunteers to identify the type of worker being sought in this ad *(a firefighter)* and talk about how firefighters help in the community.

Build Vocabulary and Concepts

Begin a discussion about the types of skills and training needed by a firefighter, the different types of work they perform, and the qualities needed to be successful at this job. Record comments in a graphic organizer as shown.

For independent practice, have students complete page 77.

FIREFIGHTERS

Job Requirements	Duties	Characteristics
knowledge of first aid	provide emergency medical care	brave
in good physical condition	drive a large truck	work well with others
able to climb	open a fire hydrant	follow directions well
good driver	spray a powerful hose	dedicated
	climb up ladders	loyal
	slide down poles	

Help Wanted!

Help your community! Engine Company No. 4 is looking for brave, strong people who can climb a ladder, drive a large vehicle, use a hose, get dressed quickly, and slide down a pole. Uniform, including helmet and boots, will be provided. Apply in person April 19th at 1625 Dalmatian Drive.

CASE #
7

Who would answer this ad?

Burnin' Hot

1. Which of the following could <u>not</u> be a firefighter?

a brave person   a blind person

a smart person   a strong person

2. Which word is an antonym for **brave**?

bright   courageous   cowardly   daring

3. Circle the word that does <u>not</u> belong.

ax   boots   hose   snorkel

4. How many words can you write that rhyme with **pole**?

_____

_____

5. On the back of this page, draw a picture of a firefighter on the job. Use these lines to write about what he or she is doing.

_____

_____

_____

_____

Help Wanted: An Archaeologist

Present the Ad

Remind students that this is a "help wanted" ad, and that they should not identify the type of worker being sought until you ask them to. Then follow these steps:

Use Picture Clues

- Ask a volunteer to describe the scene: where it is, what is happening, and how they can tell. *(in the desert; a dig or excavation; camels, palm trees, hole, shovel, and bones)*

- Ask students if they have enough information to form a hypothesis about the type of worker sought in this ad. Record any suggestions offered.

Use Text Clues

- Ask a volunteer to read the first sentence aloud and to say if it supports any of the hypotheses already proposed, or if it suggests a new one. Ask a student to explain what it means to "have a bone to pick" with someone, and how this expression might be used as a pun in this context. *(when you "have a bone to pick with someone," you have an issue to discuss with them; they are picking bones out of a dig)*

- Have another student read the rest of the ad and point out the text that provides the best clues about the type of worker sought in this ad.

Help Wanted!
If you don't think this job sounds exciting, we have a bone to pick with you! Here's your chance to travel to distant countries and learn how ancient people lived. You'll dig up dinosaur bones, mummies, and maybe buried treasure! Bring your shovel and passport to Seymour Bones Museum on June 30th.

CASE # 8
Who would answer this ad?

Present the Solution and Discuss Archaeologists

Invite volunteers to identify the type of worker being sought in this ad *(an archaeologist)* and talk about what archaeologists do.

Build Vocabulary and Concepts

Begin a discussion about archaeologists, what they do, and where they work. Record students' comments in a graphic organizer as shown.

For independent practice, have students complete page 80.

ARCHAEOLOGISTS

What They Do	Tools They Use	What They Find
excavate	picks	bones
dig for bones and artifacts	shovels	fossils
formulate and test hypotheses	screens	pottery
study ancient civilizations	microscopes	mummies
study fossils and ancient life-forms	X-ray machines	ancient building sites
	brushes	

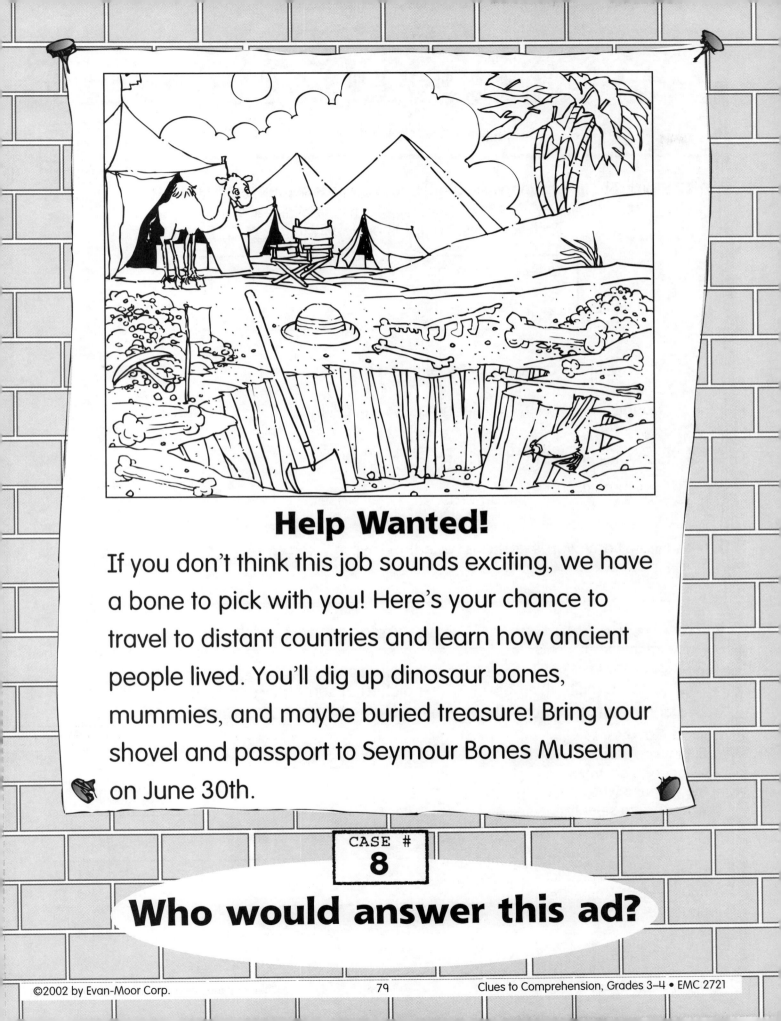

Help Wanted!

If you don't think this job sounds exciting, we have a bone to pick with you! Here's your chance to travel to distant countries and learn how ancient people lived. You'll dig up dinosaur bones, mummies, and maybe buried treasure! Bring your shovel and passport to Seymour Bones Museum on June 30th.

CASE #
8

Who would answer this ad?

©2002 by Evan-Moor Corp.

Clues to Comprehension, Grades 3–4 • EMC 2721

Dig It!

1. Which of the following could <u>not</u> complete this sentence?

Archaeologists help us understand _____.

ancient civilizations	early life-forms
electronic appliances	other cultures

2. Which word is a synonym for **exciting**?

boring   challenging   exiting   thrilling

3. Circle the word that does <u>not</u> belong.

bones   cameras   fossils   mummies

4. How many words can you write that rhyme with **bury**?

_____

_____

5. On the back of this page, draw a picture of something an archaeologist might uncover in a dig. Use these lines to write about what he or she found.

_____

_____

_____

_____

| CASE # 9 | **Help Wanted: A Cashier** |

Present the Ad

Remind students that this is a "help wanted" ad, and that they should not identify the type of worker being sought until you ask them to. Then follow these steps:

Use Picture Clues

- Invite a volunteer to describe this picture. *(a person holding a bag full of groceries)*

- Have a student read the text on the grocery bag.

- Ask students if they have enough information to form a hypothesis about the type of worker sought in this ad. Record any suggestions offered.

Use Text Clues

- Have a volunteer read the first sentence aloud, and encourage students to revise or reformulate their hypotheses.

- Ask another student to read the second sentence, and encourage students to narrow their hypotheses to grocery store jobs that require knowledge of math.

- Invite a student to read the rest of the ad and point out the text that provides the best clues about the type of worker sought in this ad.

BUY MORE GROCERY
Your Grocery SUPERSTORE

Help Wanted!
Are you good at math? Buy More Grocery Store has a full-time job available. Duties include entering prices on the cash register, and taking money, checks, and coupons from customers and giving them back correct change. We will train you. If interested, call 555-9494.

CASE # 9

Who would answer this ad?

©2002 by Evan-Moor Corp.　82　Clues to Comprehension, Grades 3–4 • EMC 2721

Present the Solution and Discuss Cashiers

Invite volunteers to identify the type of worker being sought in this ad *(a cashier)* and talk about the various duties performed by cashiers.

Build Vocabulary and Concepts

Invite students to brainstorm other jobs that require use of math skills. Record their comments in a chart as shown.

Job	Adding	Subtracting	Counting	Measuring Length	Measuring Volume	Geometry
cashier	✓	✓	✓			
bank teller	✓	✓	✓			
carpenter	✓	✓	✓	✓		✓
chef			✓		✓	

For independent practice, have students complete page 83.

Help Wanted!

Are you good at math? Buy More Grocery Store has a full-time job available. Duties include entering prices on the cash register, and taking money, checks, and coupons from customers and giving them back correct change. We will train you. If interested, call 555-9494.

CASE #
9

Who would answer this ad?

Making Change

1. Which of the following is <u>not</u> an important part of a cashier's job?

reading prices   making change

talking to people   using the Internet

2. Which word is a synonym for **duties**?

activities   favorites   responsibilities   traditions

3. Circle the word or words that do <u>not</u> belong.

calling card   cash   check   credit card

4. How many words can you write that rhyme with **cash**?

_____

_____

5. On the back of this page, draw a picture of what you would buy at the grocery store if you had $20 to spend. Use these lines to write about what you would buy.

_____

_____

_____

_____

©2002 by Evan-Moor Corp.   Clues to Comprehension, Grades 3–4 • EMC 2721

Job Wanted!

Job Wanted!

Don't have enough time to clean your house? Let me do your chores for you! I'll dust furniture, sweep and wash floors, vacuum rugs, wash and dry dishes, make the beds and do laundry. I bring my own cleaning supplies. Call Sophia at 555-7222.

CASE # 1

What job does this person want?

Job Wanted!

Abracadabra! With a wave of my magic wand, I'll make your birthday party fun. I am the Amazing Presto. My tricks include drawing your chosen card from the deck, pulling a rabbit from my hat, and making myself disappear. Call me soon at 555-1055!

CASE # 2

What job does this person want?

Job Wanted!

Do you need a vacation? Want to sail on the ocean? Ski in the mountains? Want to make travel plans to any city, state, or country in the world. I'll arrange for your tickets and transportation to the airport. Call me at 555-7879.

CASE # 3

What job does this person want?

©2002 by Evan-Moor Corp.

Clues to Comprehension, Grades 3–4 • EMC 2721

Job Wanted: A Housekeeper

Present the Ad

Tell students that this is a "job wanted" ad, written by someone who is looking for a job. Ask students not to identify the type of worker seeking a job until you ask them to. Then follow these steps:

Use Picture Clues

- Invite a volunteer to describe picture. *(a high-powered vacuum cleaner being pushed through a living room)*

- Ask students whether they have enough information to formulate a hypothesis about the type of job being sought. Record any ideas they offer.

Use Text Clues

- Have a volunteer read the first sentence, and encourage speculation about the sort of work being sought by the job-seeker who wrote this ad.

- Ask another student to read the rest of the ad and point out the text that is most helpful in identifying the type of work being sought.

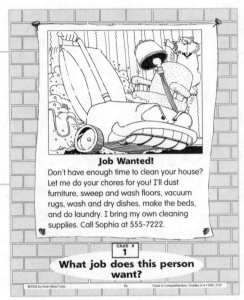

Job Wanted!
Don't have enough time to clean your house? Let me do your chores for you! I'll dust furniture, sweep and wash floors, vacuum rugs, wash and dry dishes, make the beds, and do laundry. I bring my own cleaning supplies. Call Sophia at 555-7222.

CASE #
1

What job does this person want?

©2002 by Evan-Moor Corp.   86   Clues to Comprehension, Grades 3–4 • EMC 2721

Present the Solution and Discuss Housekeepers

Invite volunteers to identify the type of worker who placed this ad *(a housekeeper)* and to share what they know about housekeepers.

Build Vocabulary and Concepts

Lead students in brainstorming about household chores—those that adults in the family do, and those that can be done by children or adults. Record their ideas in a Venn diagram as shown.

For independent practice, have students complete page 87.

Children's Housework
make the bed
empty wastebaskets
separate recycling
empty drainer or dishwasher
set & clear the table

Both
fold laundry
put away clean laundry
take garbage and recycling to curb
clean the bathroom
hang laundry on the line
sweep
clean windows

Adult's Housework
wash the laundry
cook meals
shop for food
wash the dishes
mop

Job Wanted!

Don't have enough time to clean your house? Let me do your chores for you! I'll dust furniture, sweep and wash floors, vacuum rugs, wash and dry dishes, make the beds, and do laundry. I bring my own cleaning supplies. Call Sophia at 555-7222.

CASE #
1

What job does this person want?

Cleaning Crew

1. Choose the words that <u>cannot</u> complete this sentence:

People might hire housekeepers if they _____.

don't have time to do housework	don't like to do housework
like to do everything themselves	can afford it

2. Which word is <u>not</u> a synonym for **clean**?

filthy sparkling spotless tidy

3. Circle the word that does <u>not</u> belong.

broom mop sheets vacuum

4. How many words can you write that rhyme with **clean**?

_____

_____

5. If you could hire a housekeeper to do your least favorite chore, what job would you give him or her? On the back of this page, draw a picture of the housekeeper doing your work. Then use these lines to write about it.

_____

_____

_____

_____

Job Wanted: A Magician

Present the Ad

Remind students that this is a "job wanted" ad, written by someone who is looking for a job. Ask students not to identify the type of worker seeking a job until you ask them to. Then follow these steps:

Use Picture Clues

• Ask a student to describe this picture. *(a hand, a magic wand, a hat, a rabbit)*

• Have a student read what the rabbit is saying.

• Invite students to formulate hypotheses about the type of work sought by the job-seeker who wrote this ad. Record any ideas they offer.

Use Text Clues

• Have a volunteer read the first sentence, and encourage speculation about the type of job this worker wants.

• Ask another student to read the rest of the ad and point out the text that is most helpful in identifying the type of work being sought.

O.K. WHERE AM I NOW?

Job Wanted!
Abracadabra! With a wave of my magic wand, I'll make your birthday party fun. I am the Amazing Presto. My tricks include drawing your chosen card from the deck, pulling a rabbit from my hat, and making myself disappear. Call me soon at 555-1055!

CASE # 2
What job does this person want?

©2002 by Evan-Moor Corp.   89   Clues to Comprehension, Grades 3–4 • EMC 2721

Present the Solution and Discuss Magicians

Invite volunteers to identify the type of worker who placed this ad *(a magician)* and to share any experiences they have had with magicians.

Build Vocabulary and Concepts

Tell students that magicians are a type of entertainer, as are clowns and jugglers. Lead students in discussing the similarities and differences among these entertainers, and record their comments in a three-part Venn diagram as shown.

For independent practice, have students complete page 90.

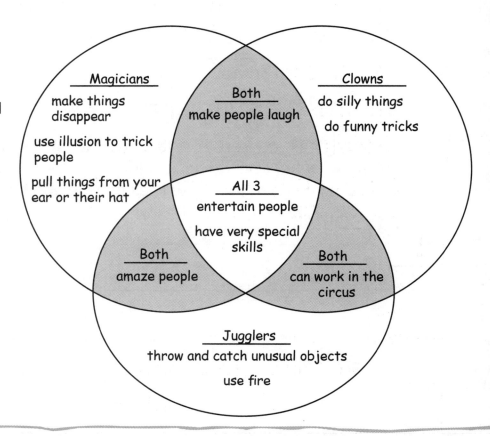

Magicians
make things disappear

use illusion to trick people

pull things from your ear or their hat

Both
make people laugh

Clowns
do silly things

do funny tricks

All 3
entertain people

have very special skills

Both
amaze people

Both
can work in the circus

Jugglers
throw and catch unusual objects

use fire

Job Wanted!

Abracadabra! With a wave of my magic wand, I'll make your birthday party fun. I am the Amazing Presto. My tricks include drawing your chosen card from the deck, pulling a rabbit from my hat, and making myself disappear. Call me soon at 555-1055!

CASE #
2

What job does this person want?

Abracadabra!

1. Choose the best word to complete this sentence:

Magicians really use _____ , not magic, to do their tricks.

| illusions | rabbits | science | volunteers |

2. Which prefix can you use to make an antonym for **appear**?

un-   in-   re-   dis-

3. Circle the word that does <u>not</u> belong.

hat   rabbit   turkey   wand

4. How many words can you write that rhyme with **trick**?

_____

_____

5. What would you like to see a magician pull out of a hat? Draw a picture of it on the back of this page, and then use these lines to write about this magic trick.

_____

_____

_____

_____

_____

Present the Ad

Remind students that this is a "job wanted" ad, written by someone who is looking for a job. Ask students not to identify the type of worker seeking a job until you ask them to. Then follow these steps:

Use Picture Clues

- Ask a student to describe this picture. *(two people and a dog thinking about places to visit)*

- Have a student read the text on the brochure the people are looking at.

- Ask students if they have enough information to formulate a hypothesis about the type of work sought by the job-seeker who wrote this ad. Record any ideas they offer.

Use Text Clues

- Have a volunteer read the first sentence, and encourage speculation about the type of job this worker wants.

- Ask another student to read the next three sentences, and encourage students to confirm or revise their hypotheses.

- Invite a student to read the rest of the ad aloud and point out the text that is most helpful in identifying the type of work being sought.

Job Wanted!
Do you need a vacation? Want to sail on the ocean? Ski in the mountains? Go on a safari? I can help you make travel plans to any city, state, or country in the world. I'll arrange for your tickets and transportation to the airport. Call me at 555-7879.

CASE #
3

What job does this person want?

©2002 by Evan-Moor Corp.   92   Clues to Comprehension, Grades 3–4 • EMC 2721

Present the Solution and Discuss Travel Agents

Invite volunteers to identify the type of worker who placed this ad *(a travel agent)* and to share anything they know about travel agents and their work.

Build Vocabulary and Concepts

Ask students to imagine that a travel agent is going to help them plan a trip to anywhere in the world. If possible, have a world map or globe available for reference. Then record the places students would like to visit, according to their location within the four hemispheres as shown.

For independent practice, have students complete page 93.

NORTH		
Mount McKinley (Alaska)		
Seattle		
the Great Lakes		

WEST			EAST
	Hawai'i	New York City	
	Samoa	Taiwan	
	Hollywood	India	

	Galápagos Islands	
	Antarctica	
	the Amazon Jungle	
SOUTH		

Job Wanted!

Do you need a vacation? Want to sail on the ocean? Ski in the mountains? Go on a safari? I can help you make travel plans to any city, state, or country in the world. I'll arrange for your tickets and transportation to the airport. Call me at 555-7879.

CASE #
3

What job does this person want?

©2002 by Evan-Moor Corp.

Clues to Comprehension, Grades 3–4 • EMC 2721

Bon Voyage!

1. Choose the word that <u>cannot</u> be used to complete this sentence:

A travel agent can help you make _____ reservations.

airplane	hotel	dinner	train

2. Which word is <u>not</u> a synonym for **trip**?

excursion　　　　journey　　　　route　　　　voyage

3. Circle the word that does <u>not</u> belong.

boat　　　　rocket　　　　plane　　　　train

4. Which prefix can you add to **arrange** to make a word that means "to arrange again"?

dis-　　　　pre-　　　　re-　　　　un-

5. On the back of this page, draw a picture postcard from a place you would like to visit. Use these lines to write the text of the postcard. Don't forget to begin with **Dear**, and to close with **Yours truly**, **Love**, or another closing.

_____

_____

_____

_____

_____

Job Wanted: A Dog Trainer

Present the Ad

Remind students that this is a "job wanted" ad, written by someone who is looking for a job. Ask students not to identify the type of worker seeking a job until you ask them to. Then follow these steps:

Use Picture Clues

- Invite a student to say what is happening in this picture. *(a person is giving a dog a command)*

- Ask another student to read the text in the picture and to speculate about the type of work sought by the job-seeker who wrote this ad. Record any ideas offered.

Use Text Clues

- Have a volunteer read the first two sentences and explain the puns. *("In the doghouse" means "in trouble." "Barking up the wrong tree" means "making a mistake." They're humorous because the subject deals with dogs.)*

- Ask another student to read the next sentence and formulate or revise the hypotheses about the type of worker who placed this ad.

- Invite a student to read the rest of the ad aloud and point out the text that is most helpful in identifying the type of work being sought.

STAY, BRUTUS!

Job Wanted!

Is your dog in the doghouse because it doesn't behave? If you think your veterinarian can help you, you're barking up the wrong tree. Call me instead! I can teach your dog to obey easy commands like "sit," "come," "down," and much more! Call Jessica at 555-2945.

CASE # **4**

What job does this person want?

©2002 by Evan-Moor Corp.   95   Clues to Comprehension, Grades 3-4 • EMC 2721

Present the Solution and Discuss Dog Trainers

Invite volunteers to identify the type of worker who placed this ad *(a dog trainer)* and to share anything they know about training dogs.

Build Vocabulary and Concepts

Encourage students to brainstorm other commands often given to dogs and to explain the behavior that is expected after each command. Record their ideas in a T-chart as shown.

For independent practice, have students complete page 96.

Command	Behavior
stay	dog does not move
heel	dog stands beside you
fetch	dog brings something to you
roll over	dog lies on back
beg	dog sits on hind legs with front paws in the air

Job Wanted!

Is your dog in the doghouse because it doesn't behave? If you think your veterinarian can help you, you're barking up the wrong tree. Call me instead! I can teach your dog to obey easy commands like "sit," "come," "down," and much more! Call Jessica at 555-2945.

CASE #
4

What job does this person want?

©2002 by Evan-Moor Corp.

Clues to Comprehension, Grades 3–4 • EMC 2721

Fetch!

1. Choose the word that best completes this sentence:

A dog trainer's job is to _____ dogs.

feed	heal	scold	teach

2. Choose the best pair of words to fill in these blanks:

A **doctor** is for **people** as a _____ is for _____ .

chef / food	surgeon / stitches
tank / fish	veterinarian / animals

3. Circle the word that does <u>not</u> belong.

collar   tail   leash   dish

4. Which prefix can you add to **obey** to make its antonym?

dis-   pre-   re-   un-

5. On the back of this page, draw a picture of a trick you would teach your dog if you had one. Use these lines to write the command you would give to get your dog to do this trick.

_____

_____

_____

_____

Job Wanted: A Baby-Sitter

Present the Ad

Remind students that this is a "job wanted" ad, written by someone who is looking for a job. Ask students not to identify the type of worker seeking a job until you ask them to. Then follow these steps:

Use Picture Clues

- Invite a student to describe what is happening in this picture. *(A child is chasing a cat and dog through a house, making a mess. A woman is watching in disbelief.)*

- Ask students if they have enough information to formulate a hypothesis about the type of work sought by the job-seeker who wrote this ad. Record any ideas they offer.

Use Text Clues

- Have a volunteer read the first sentence, and encourage speculation about the type of job being sought.

- Ask another student to read the next two sentences and explain what "fly off the handle" and "lend you a hand" mean. *(lose your temper; give you some help)* Invite students to confirm or revise any hypotheses they have formulated.

- Invite a student to read the rest of the ad aloud and point out the text that is most helpful in identifying the type of work being sought.

Job Wanted!

Are your kids driving you crazy? Don't fly off the handle—call me! I'll lend you a hand. Dependable teenager looking for after-school job. If you need to leave the house, I'll watch your children while you're gone. $5 an hour. Available weekends too! Call Pat at 555-2928.

CASE #
5

What job does this person want?

©2002 by Evan-Moor Corp. • 98 • Clues to Comprehension, Grades 3-4 • EMC 2721

Present the Solution and Discuss Baby-Sitters

Invite volunteers to identify the type of worker who placed this ad *(a baby-sitter)* and to share their experiences with baby-sitters.

Build Vocabulary and Concepts

Lead students in brainstorming about baby-sitters. Record their ideas in a graphic organizer as shown.

For independent practice, have students complete page 99.

BABY-SITTERS

Who They Might Be	What They Do	What They Need to Know
a friend of the family	play games with you	what to do in an emergency
a neighbor	read to you	how to change a diaper
a teenager	watch a movie with you	how to entertain kids
a grandmother	make food and snacks for you	how to have fun
	tell you stories	

Job Wanted!

Are your kids driving you crazy? Don't fly off the handle—call me! I'll lend you a hand. Dependable teenager looking for after-school job. If you need to leave the house, I'll watch your children while you're gone. $5 an hour. Available weekends too! Call Pat at 555-2928.

CASE #
5

What job does this person want?

Bedtime!

1. Choose the words that <u>cannot</u> complete this sentence:

A good baby-sitter makes you _____ .

feel comfortable	follow directions
very scared	yummy treats

2. Which word is <u>not</u> a compound word?

childcare   helper   teenage   weekend

3. Circle the words that do <u>not</u> belong.

make a snack   read a story   start a fire   watch a movie

4. Which prefix can you add to **available** to make its antonym?

dis-   pre-   re-   un-

5. On the back of this page, draw a picture of something you like to do with your favorite baby-sitter. Use these lines to write about it.

_____

_____

_____

_____

_____

Job Wanted: A Baker

Present the Ad

Remind students that this is a "job wanted" ad, written by someone who is looking for a job. Ask students not to identify the type of worker seeking a job until you ask them to. Then follow these steps.

Use Picture Clues

- Ask a student to describe this picture. *(two people and a wedding cake)*

- Ask students if they have enough information to formulate a hypothesis about the type of work sought by the job-seeker who wrote this ad. Record any ideas they offer.

Use Text Clues

- Have a volunteer read the first sentence and explain the pun. *("A piece of cake" means "very easy." It's funny because this ad is about cakes.)*

- Invite a student to read the rest of the ad aloud and point out the text that is most helpful in identifying the type of work being sought.

Job Wanted!

Planning your wedding is a piece of cake when you call me. I make wedding cakes that will make your mouth water. Price depends on size, ingredients, and flavor. Call Icing on the Cake at 555-3221.

CASE # 6

What job does this person want?

©2002 by Evan-Moor Corp. 101 Clues to Comprehension, Grades 3–4 • EMC 2721

Present the Solution and Discuss Bakers

Invite volunteers to identify the type of worker who placed this ad *(a baker)* and to share what they know about bakers.

Build Vocabulary and Concepts

Encourage students to brainstorm items prepared by bakers. Record their ideas in a graphic organizer as shown.

For independent practice, have students complete page 102.

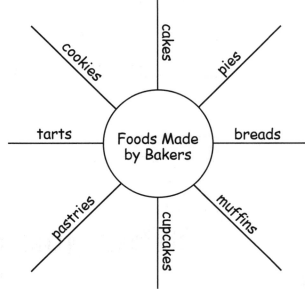

cookies · cakes · pies · tarts · Foods Made by Bakers · breads · pastries · cupcakes · muffins

Job Wanted!

Planning your wedding is a piece of cake when you call me. I make wedding cakes that will make your mouth water. Price depends on size, ingredients, and flavor. Call Icing on the Cake at 555-3221.

CASE #
6

What job does this person want?

Piece of Cake

1. Choose the best pair of words to complete this sentence:

A **baker** is to a **bakery** as a _____ is to a _____ .

grocer / grocery	librarian / library
barber / barb	racer / race

2. Which of these is a synonym for **icing**?

cake   ice cream   frosting   sugar

3. Circle the word that does <u>not</u> belong.

bread   cake   pie   stew

4. How many words can you write that rhyme with **cake**?

_____

_____

5. On the back of this page, draw a picture of your favorite thing to buy at a bakery. Use these lines to write about your favorite item and the ingredients used to make it.

_____

_____

_____

_____

Job Wanted: A Dog Groomer

Present the Ad

Remind students that this is a "job wanted" ad, written by someone who is looking for a job. Ask students not to identify the type of worker seeking a job until you ask them to. Then follow these steps:

Use Picture Clues

- Ask a student to describe this picture. *(a dog and a bird sitting out in the rain)*

- Ask students if they have enough information to formulate a hypothesis about the type of work sought by the job-seeker who wrote this ad. Record any ideas they offer.

Use Text Clues

- Have a volunteer read the first two sentences and explain the pun. *("Gone to the dogs" means "been ruined." It's funny because this ad is about dogs.)*

- Ask another student to read the third sentence aloud and speculate about the identity of the worker who placed this ad.

- Invite a student to read the rest of the ad aloud and point out the text that is most helpful in identifying the type of work being sought.

Job Wanted!

Has your pooch's appearance gone to the dogs? Let me give you a hand. My services include washing and drying, trimming and brushing hair, and clipping nails. $45 for all breeds. Call Kristen at It's Raining Cats and Dogs for an appointment at 555-7274.

CASE # 7

What job does this person want?

©2002 by Evan-Moor Corp.   104   Clues to Comprehension, Grades 3-4 • EMC 2721

Present the Solution and Discuss Dog Groomers

Invite volunteers to identify the type of worker who placed this ad *(a dog groomer)* and to share what they know about dog groomers and their work.

Build Vocabulary and Concepts

Lead students in brainstorming different breeds of dogs and recording their characteristics in a chart as shown.

Breed	Short hair	Long hair	Curly hair	Straight hair	Long ears	Short ears	Short tail	Long tail
poodle	✓		✓		✓		✓	
dachshund	✓			✓	✓			✓
German shepherd	✓			✓		✓		✓
Pekingese		✓		✓	✓			✓

For independent practice, have students complete page 105.

Job Wanted!

Has your pooch's appearance gone to the dogs? Let me give you a hand. My services include washing and drying, trimming and brushing hair, and clipping nails. $45 for all breeds. Call Kristen at It's Raining Cats and Dogs for an appointment at 555-7274.

CASE #
7

What job does this person want?

Name ________________________________

Gone to the Dogs

CASE # 7

1. Choose the word that <u>cannot</u> complete this sentence:

Dog groomers ____________________ dogs.

brush	dry	shampoo	train

2. Which word is a synonym for **breed**?

brand   race   style   type

3. Circle the word that does <u>not</u> belong.

clip   cut   fold   trim

4. How many words can you write that rhyme with **dog**?

____

____

5. On the back of this page, draw a picture of your favorite type of dog. Use these lines to write about what breed of dog it is and what its name is.

____

____

____

____

____

For Sale!

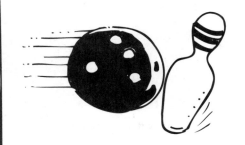

For Sale!
Winter decoration for your yard. Figure made entirely of snow. Has top, middle, and bottom sections. Button eyes and carrot nose. Wears black top hat and red scarf. Hurry before it melts away! Call 555-1791.

CASE #
1

What item is for sale?

For Sale!
You'll want to see what pops up when you use this small kitchen appliance. You can control how light or dark the bread gets. It's perfect for making toast, bagels, and even waffles for breakfast. $5 or best offer. Call Mr. Crumb at 555-3941.

CASE #
2

What item is for sale?

For Sale!
Portable source of light. Runs on two "C" batteries. Shines up to 20 feet. Has high- and low-beam switch. Perfect for camping or during storms when your electricity goes out. $___ or best offer. Call Gayle at 555-2486.

CASE #
4

What item is for sale?

For Sale: A Snowman

Present the Ad

Tell students that this is a "for sale" ad, written by someone who has an item to sell. Ask students not to identify the item being offered for sale until you ask them to. Then follow these steps:

Use Picture Clues

- Ask a student to describe the scene in this picture. *(Two children are rolling giant snowballs outdoors in a snowstorm.)*

- Ask students if they have enough information to formulate a hypothesis about the item that is being offered for sale. Record any ideas they offer.

Use Text Clues

- Have a volunteer read the first sentence and speculate about what the item on sale might be.

- Ask another student to read the second sentence aloud and revise or formulate hypotheses about the item.

- Invite a student to read the rest of the ad aloud and point out the text that is most helpful in identifying the item being offered for sale.

For Sale!
Winter decoration for your yard. Figure made entirely of snow. Has top, middle, and bottom sections. Button eyes and carrot nose. Wears black top hat and red scarf. Hurry before it melts away! Call 555-1791.

CASE # 1
What item is for sale?

©2002 by Evan-Moor Corp.   108   Clues to Comprehension, Grades 3–4 • EMC 2721

Present the Solution and Discuss Snowmen

Invite volunteers to identify the item offered for sale in this ad *(a snowman)* and to share what they know about snowmen.

Build Vocabulary and Concepts

Remind students that snow is one of the many forms that water can take. Lead students in brainstorming names for water in its liquid, solid, and vapor forms. Record their comments in a graphic organizer as shown.

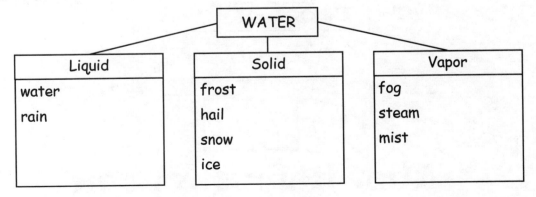

WATER		
Liquid	**Solid**	**Vapor**
water	frost	fog
rain	hail	steam
	snow	mist
	ice	

For independent practice, have students complete page 109.

For Sale!

Winter decoration for your yard. Figure made entirely of snow. Has top, middle, and bottom sections. Button eyes and carrot nose. Wears black top hat and red scarf. Hurry before it melts away! Call 555-1791.

CASE #
1

What item is for sale?

©2002 by Evan-Moor Corp.
Clues to Comprehension, Grades 3–4 • EMC 2721

Meltdown

1. Choose the word that <u>cannot</u> complete this sentence:

Melted snow turns into _____.

| frost | puddles | slush | water |

2. Which word is an antonym for **melt**?

jell   fry   freeze   smell

3. Circle the word that does <u>not</u> belong.

button   cane   hat   scarf

4. How many words can you write that rhyme with **snow**?

_____

_____

5. On the back of this page, draw a picture of a snowman you would like to make. Use these lines to write about where you would like to be when you make this snowman.

_____

_____

_____

_____

For Sale: A Toaster

Present the Ad

Remind students that this is a "for sale" ad, written by someone who has an item to sell. Ask students not to identify the item being offered for sale until you ask them to. Then follow these steps:

Use Picture Clues

• Ask a student to describe this picture. *(two cats looking at packages of food on a kitchen counter; the cord for an electric appliance)*

• Ask students if they have enough information to formulate a hypothesis about the item that is being offered for sale. Record any ideas they offer.

Use Text Clues

• Have a volunteer read the first sentence and speculate about the item offered for sale.

• Ask another student to read the rest of the ad aloud and point out the text that is most helpful in identifying the item being offered for sale.

For Sale!
You'll want to see what pops up when you use this small kitchen appliance. You can control how light or dark the bread gets. It's perfect for making toast, bagels, and even waffles for breakfast. $5 or best offer. Call Mr. Crumb at 555-3941.

What item is for sale?

Present the Solution and Discuss Toasters

Invite volunteers to identify the item offered for sale in this ad *(a toaster)* and to share what they know about toasters.

Build Vocabulary and Concepts

Tell students that a toaster is an electrical appliance used in the kitchen. Invite students to brainstorm other kitchen appliances and to record their uses on a chart as shown.

Appliance	Blend	Chop	Cut	Cook	Toast
blender	✓	✓	✓		
toaster				✓	✓
microwave oven				✓	
mixer	✓				
can opener			✓		

For independent practice, have students complete page 112.

For Sale!

You'll want to see what pops up when you use this small kitchen appliance. You can control how light or dark the bread gets. It's perfect for making toast, bagels, and even waffles for breakfast. $5 or best offer. Call Mr. Crumb at 555-3941.

CASE #
2

What item is for sale?

Pop-Ups

1. Choose the word that <u>cannot</u> complete this sentence:

Toast with _____ is tasty.

| butter | honey | jam | lemon |

2. Circle the best pair of words to complete this sentence:

Breakfast is to **morning** as _____ is to _____.

| dinner / evening | snack / cookies |
| tea / coffee | waffle / toaster |

3. Circle the word that does <u>not</u> belong.

bagel   pancake   toast   waffle

4. How many words can you write that rhyme with **crumb**?

_____

_____

5. What is your favorite thing to put on toast? Write about it on these lines.

_____

_____

_____

For Sale: A Desk

Present the Ad

Remind students that this is a "for sale" ad, written by someone who has an item to sell. Ask students not to identify the item being offered for sale until you ask them to. Then follow these steps:

Use Picture Clues

- Ask a student to describe the scene in the picture. *(a girl doing schoolwork in a bathtub)*

- Ask students if they have enough information to formulate a hypothesis about the item that is being offered for sale. Record any ideas they offer.

Use Text Clues

- Have a volunteer read the first sentence and speculate about the item offered for sale.

- Ask another student to read the rest of the ad aloud and point out the text that is most helpful in identifying the item being offered for sale.

For Sale!
Does the student in your family need a place to study and do homework? This furniture is just right! Made of oak with four drawers and matching chair. Lamp included. $75. Call 555-8788.

CASE #
3
What item is for sale?

©2002 by Evan-Moor Corp. 113 Clues to Comprehension, Grades 3–4 • EMC 2721

Present the Solution and Discuss Desks

Invite volunteers to identify the item offered for sale in this ad *(a desk)* and to share their experiences with desks.

Build Vocabulary and Concepts

Tell students that a desk is one item that is useful to have when doing homework. Invite students to mention other things that they like to have available when doing homework. Record them in a graphic organizer as shown.

For independent practice, have students complete page 115.

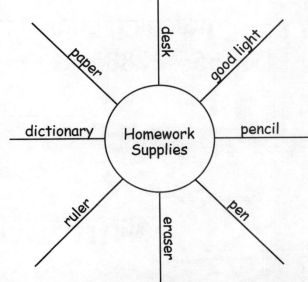

paper · desk · good light · dictionary · Homework Supplies · pencil · ruler · eraser · pen

For Sale!

Does the student in your family need a place to study and do homework? This furniture is just right! Made of oak with four drawers and matching chair. Lamp included. $75. Call 555-8788.

CASE #

3

What item is for sale?

Hit the Books

1. Choose the word that <u>cannot</u> complete this sentence:

A desk is a good place to _____ .

| read | sleep | study | write |

2. Circle the best pair of words to complete this sentence:

Desk is to **classroom** as _____ is to _____ .

| air / tire | bed / bedroom |
| swing / swingset | pig / pigpen |

3. Circle the word that does <u>not</u> belong.

chair   desk   lamp   television

4. How many words can you write that rhyme with **study**?

_____

_____

5. Where do you like to study, read, or do homework? Draw a picture of yourself there on the back of this page. Use these lines to write about where you are.

_____

_____

_____

_____

©2002 by Evan-Moor Corp.
Clues to Comprehension, Grades 3–4 • EMC 2721

CASE # 4 — For Sale: A Flashlight

Present the Ad

Remind students that this is a "for sale" ad, written by someone who has an item to sell. Ask students not to identify the item being offered for sale until you ask them to. Then follow these steps:

Use Picture Clues

- Ask a student to describe the scene in the picture. *(a camper shining a flashlight on a bear that is getting into a box of food)*

- Ask students if they have enough information to formulate a hypothesis about the item that is being offered for sale. Record any ideas they offer.

Use Text Clues

- Have a volunteer read the first sentence and speculate about the item offered for sale.

- Ask another student to read the rest of the ad aloud and point out the text that is most helpful in identifying the item being offered for sale.

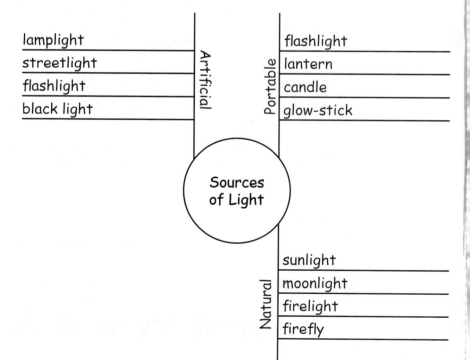

For Sale!
Portable source of light. Runs on two "C" batteries. Shines up to 20 feet. Has high- and low-beam switch. Perfect for camping or during storms when your electricity goes out. $10 or best offer. Call Gayle at 555-2486.

CASE # 4
What item is for sale?

Present the Solution and Discuss Flashlights

Invite volunteers to identify the item offered for sale in this ad *(a flashlight)* and to share what they know about flashlights.

Build Vocabulary and Concepts

Refer back to the first sentence of the ad, reminding students that a flashlight is described as "a portable source of light." Lead students in brainstorming other sources of light, and record them on a graphic organizer as shown.

For independent practice, have students complete page 118.

Artificial
lamplight
streetlight
flashlight
black light

Portable
flashlight
lantern
candle
glow-stick

Sources of Light

Natural
sunlight
moonlight
firelight
firefly

For Sale!

Portable source of light. Runs on two "C" batteries. Shines up to 20 feet. Has high- and low-beam switch. Perfect for camping or during storms when your electricity goes out. $10 or best offer. Call Gayle at 555-2486.

CASE #
4

What item is for sale?

©2002 by Evan-Moor Corp.

In the Dark

1. Choose the best word to complete this sentence:

You can use a flashlight to _____ the darkness.

discover	illuminate	shine	warm

2. Which word is <u>not</u> a synonym for **darkness**?

brightness   dimness   gloom   murkiness

3. Circle the word that does <u>not</u> belong.

battery   light bulb   match   switch

4. How many words can you write that rhyme with **light**?

_____

_____

5. What would you like to use to light your house if the power goes out? Draw it on the back of this page, and then write about it on these lines.

_____

_____

_____

_____

For Sale: A Bowling Ball

Present the Ad

Remind students that this is a "for sale" ad, written by someone who has an item to sell. Ask students not to identify the item being offered for sale until you ask them to. Then follow these steps:

Use Picture Clues

- Invite a student to describe the setting in this picture. *(a bowling alley)*

- Ask students if they have enough information to formulate a hypothesis about the item that is being offered for sale. Record any ideas they offer.

Use Text Clues

- Have a volunteer read the first two sentences and explain the pun. *("Up your alley" means "just the thing for you." It is funny because the setting is a bowling alley.)*

- Ask another student to read the rest of the ad aloud and point out the text that is most helpful in identifying the item being offered for sale.

For Sale!
Are you interested in learning a new sport? This might be right up your alley! 10-pound sports ball for left-handed person. Black with three finger holes. Never used. It just might help you get a strike or spare in every frame! Call Art at 555-1971.

CASE #
5

What item is for sale?

©2002 by Evan-Moor Corp.   120   Clues to Comprehension, Grades 3-4 • EMC 2721

Present the Solution and Discuss Bowling Balls

Invite volunteers to identify the item offered for sale in this ad *(a bowling ball)* and to share what they know about bowling.

Build Vocabulary and Concepts

Invite students to brainstorm other games played with balls. Record their comments in a graphic organizer as shown.

For independent practice, have students complete page 121.

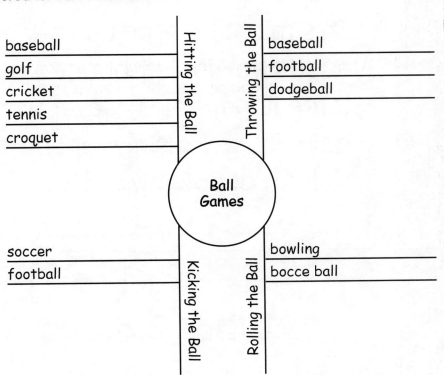

Hitting the Ball	Throwing the Ball
baseball	baseball
golf	football
cricket	dodgeball
tennis	
croquet	

Ball Games

Kicking the Ball	Rolling the Ball
soccer	bowling
football	bocce ball

For Sale!

Are you interested in learning a new sport? This might be right up your alley! 10-pound sports ball for left-handed person. Black with three finger holes. Never used. It just might help you get a strike or spare in every frame! Call Art at 555-1971.

CASE #
5

What item is for sale?

Strike!

1. Choose the word that <u>cannot</u> complete this sentence:

Bowling is a type of _____ .

entertainment	game	job	sport

2. Circle information about the bowling ball that is <u>not</u> correct.

It's black.   It's brand new.

It's for a right-handed person.   It weighs 10 pounds.

3. Circle the word that does <u>not</u> belong.

alley   backyard   lane   pin

4. How many words can you write that rhyme with **bowl**?

_____

_____

5. What sport do you like to play using a ball? Draw a picture of it on the back of this page, and then write about it on these lines.

_____

_____

_____

_____

For Sale: A Rabbit

Present the Ad

Remind students that this is a "for sale" ad, written by someone who has an item to sell. Ask students not to identify the item being offered for sale until you ask them to. Then follow these steps:

Use Picture Clues

- Ask a student to describe the expression on the face of the boy and the animals, and to say why they look that way. *(They're surprised or worried because the cage door is open and the cage is empty.)*

- Invite students to speculate about what sort of animal lived in this cage, and to say which clues in the picture support their ideas.

- Ask students if they have enough information to formulate a hypothesis about the item that is being offered for sale. Record any ideas they offer.

Use Text Clues

- Have a volunteer read the first two sentences and speculate about the item being offered for sale.

- Ask another student to read the rest of the ad aloud and point out the text that is most helpful in identifying the item being offered for sale.

- Invite a volunteer to point out and explain the pun in this ad. *("Hop to it" means "get going." It's funny because the ad is about a rabbit, and rabbits hop.)*

Present the Solution and Discuss Rabbits

Invite volunteers to identify the item offered for sale in this ad *(a rabbit)* and to share what they know about rabbits.

Build Vocabulary and Concepts

Invite students to brainstorm other animals that can be pets. Record their comments in a graphic organizer as shown.

For independent practice, have students complete page 124.

For Sale!
Moving out of state. Must sell my adorable pet, Hopper. Has brown and white fur, floppy ears, and long whiskers. Enjoys eating carrots and lettuce. Cage included. If you can provide a good home, hop to it and call me at 555-6941!

CASE # 6

What item is for sale?

©2002 by Evan-Moor Corp.   123   Clues to Comprehension, Grades 3–4 • EMC 2721

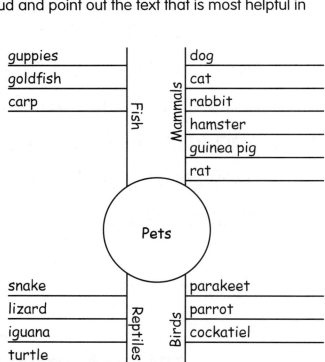

Fish		Mammals
guppies		dog
goldfish		cat
carp		rabbit
		hamster
		guinea pig
		rat

Pets

Reptiles		Birds
snake		parakeet
lizard		parrot
iguana		cockatiel
turtle		

For Sale!

Moving out of state. Must sell my adorable pet, Hopper. Has brown and white fur, floppy ears, and long whiskers. Enjoys eating carrots and lettuce. Cage included. If you can provide a good home, hop to it and call me at 555-6941!

CASE #
6

What item is for sale?

Hop Along

1. Choose the best word to complete this sentence:

A rabbit makes a good _____.

cake	pet	student	toy

2. Circle information about the rabbit that is <u>not</u> correct.

It's brown and white.   It comes with a cage.

It has short ears.   It has long whiskers.

3. Circle the word that does <u>not</u> belong.

ears   mustache   tail   whiskers

4. Which word is a synonym for **adorable**?

cruel   hateful   darling   wacky

5. Imagine you had a cage like the one on page 123. On the back of this page, draw a picture of the animal that you would like to keep in there as a pet. Use these lines to write about it.

_____

_____

_____

_____

_____

For Sale: A Violin

Present the Ad

Remind students that this is a "for sale" ad, written by someone who has an item to sell. Ask students not to identify the item being offered for sale until you ask them to. Then follow these steps:

Use Picture Clues

- Ask a student to describe what the man and the cat are doing and why, and to indicate what clues in the picture support his or her response. *(covering their ears because of an unpleasant sound; the funny-looking musical notes)*

- Ask students if they have enough information to formulate a hypothesis about the item that is being offered for sale. Record any ideas they offer.

Use Text Clues

- Have a volunteer read the first sentence and speculate about the item being offered for sale.

- Ask another student to read the second sentence, and record the names of wooden musical instruments suggested by volunteers.

- Invite another student to read the rest of the ad aloud and revise hypotheses according to the new information.

- Invite a volunteer to point out and explain the pun in this ad. *("Don't fiddle around" means "don't waste any time." It's funny because the ad is about a violin or fiddle.)*

For Sale!
Parent looking for some peace and quiet. Selling child's wooden musical instrument. Has four strings and a bow, and nestles nicely under the chin. $50. If you're interested, don't fiddle around—call me today at 555-9142!

CASE #
7

What item is for sale?

Present the Solution and Discuss Violins

Invite volunteers to identify the item offered for sale in this ad *(a violin)* and to share what they know about violins.

Build Vocabulary and Concepts

Refer back to the list of wooden instruments brainstormed by students and categorize them on a T-chart as shown. Encourage students to add other instruments to the chart as well.

For independent practice, have students complete page 127.

| WOODEN MUSICAL INSTRUMENTS ||
String Instruments	Other Wooden Instruments
bass	recorder
cello	marimba
violin	flute
viola	clarinet
guitar	piano
banjo	
ehr-hu	
koto	

For Sale!

Parent looking for some peace and quiet. Selling child's wooden musical instrument. Has four strings and a bow, and nestles nicely under the chin. $50. If you're interested, don't fiddle around—call me today at 555-9142!

CASE #
7

What item is for sale?

©2002 by Evan-Moor Corp.

Clues to Comprehension, Grades 3–4 • EMC 2721

Name ____________________

Bow and Strings

CASE # 7

1. Choose the word that cannot complete this sentence:

A violin is a ____________ instrument.

brass	musical	string	wooden

2. Which word is an antonym for **quiet**?

calm noisy quite soft

3. Circle the word that does not belong.

cello viola violin trumpet

4. How many words can you write that rhyme with **string**?

____

____

5. Draw a picture of an instrument that you play or would like to learn to play. Use these lines to write about it.

____

____

____

____

____

©2002 by Evan-Moor Corp.

For Sale: An Alarm Clock

Present the Ad

Remind students that this is a "for sale" ad, written by someone who has an item to sell. Ask students not to identify the item being offered for sale until you ask them to. Then follow these steps:

Use Picture Clues

- Ask a student to describe the scene in the picture *(a boy, cat, dog, and fish all fast asleep; a school bus passing by outside)* and say what is happening. *(The boy has overslept.)*

- Ask students if they have enough information to formulate a hypothesis about the item that is being offered for sale. Record any ideas they offer.

Use Text Clues

- Have a volunteer read the first sentence and speculate about the item being offered for sale.

- Ask another student to read the rest of the ad aloud and point out the text that is most helpful in identifying the item being offered for sale.

- Invite a volunteer to explain the meaning of "by the skin of your teeth." *("just barely")*

For Sale!

Are you tired of waking up late every morning? Do you catch the school bus just by the skin of your teeth? This noisy timepiece is just what you need to get you going! You set the time you want to wake up, and it keeps ringing until you shut it off. Asking $10. Call Belle at 555-6943.

CASE 8
8

What item is for sale?

©2002 by Evan-Moor Corp.   129   Clues to Comprehension, Grades 3-4 • EMC 2721

Present the Solution and Discuss Alarm Clocks

Invite volunteers to identify the item offered for sale in this ad *(an alarm clock)* and to share their experiences with alarm clocks.

Build Vocabulary and Concepts

Invite students to brainstorm other ways to keep track of time. Record their comments in a graphic organizer as shown.

For independent practice, have students complete page 130.

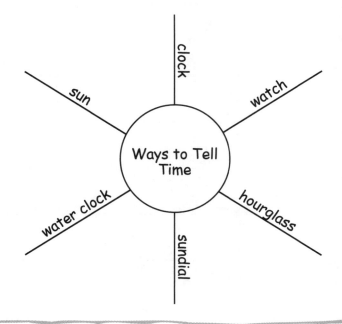

clock
sun
watch

Ways to Tell Time

water clock
hourglass
sundial

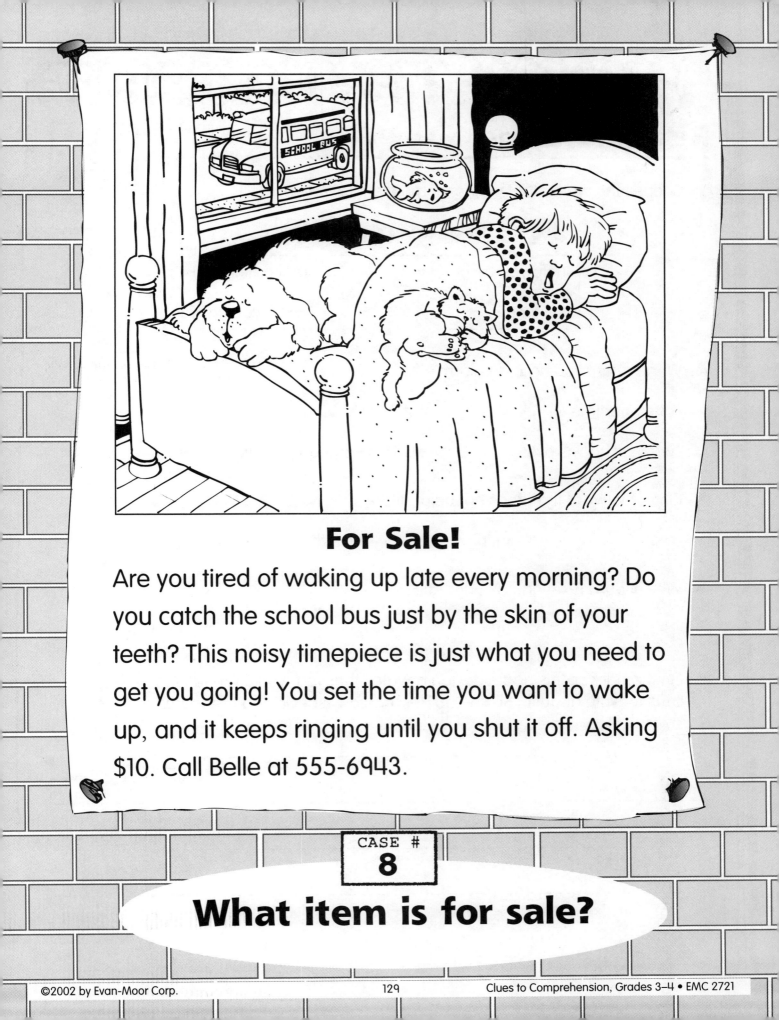

For Sale!

Are you tired of waking up late every morning? Do you catch the school bus just by the skin of your teeth? This noisy timepiece is just what you need to get you going! You set the time you want to wake up, and it keeps ringing until you shut it off. Asking $10. Call Belle at 555-6943.

CASE #
8

What item is for sale?

Rise and Shine

1. Choose the words that <u>cannot</u> complete this sentence:

You can use an alarm clock to _____ .

help you be on time	make dinner
tell time	wake you up

2. When might you hear an alarm?

at dinnertime   if there's a fire

when school is over   when someone's at your door

3. Circle the word that does <u>not</u> belong.

alarm   digital   grandfather   uncle

4. Which word is an antonym for **late**?

before   early   later   swift

5. On the back of this page, design a watch that you would like to wear. Use these
lines to write about it. Be sure to describe any special features it has.

_____

_____

_____

_____

For Sale: A Cow and a Calf

Present the Ad

Remind students that this is a "for sale" ad, written by someone who has an item to sell. Ask students not to identify the item being offered for sale until you ask them to. Then follow these steps:

Use Picture Clues

- Ask a student to describe the setting in the picture and to indicate the picture clues that helped determine the setting. *(a farm; barn, hay, tractor)*

- Invite a student to read the sign in the picture, to point out what is unusual about the text, and how it might relate to the rest of the scene. *("Moving" is spelled with an extra "o." It contains the word "moo," which is the sound made by a cow.)*

- Ask students if they have enough information to formulate a hypothesis about the items that are being offered for sale. Record any ideas they offer.

Use Text Clues

- Have a volunteer read the first two sentences and speculate about the items being offered for sale.

- Ask another student to read the third sentence and then name milk-producing animals. *(cow, goat, sheep)*

- Invite a student to read the rest of the ad aloud and point out the text that is most helpful in identifying the items being offered for sale.

For Sale!
Mooving sale! Retired farmer must sell barnyard animals. Needs to find a good home for milk-producing animal and her offspring. Won blue ribbons at County Fair. Both are white with black spots. Make me an offer. Call 555-5934.

CASE #
9

What is for sale?

©2002 by Evan-Moor Corp.   132   Clues to Comprehension, Grades 3–4 • EMC 2721

Present the Solution and Discuss Cows and Calves

Invite volunteers to identify the items offered for sale in this ad *(a cow and a calf)* and to share what they know about cows and calves.

Build Vocabulary and Concepts

Invite students to brainstorm other farm animals and the products we get from them. Record their comments in a T-chart as shown.

For independent practice, have students complete page 133.

Farm Animals	Products
cow	milk, butter, cheese, yogurt, cream
chicken	eggs, feathers, meat
sheep	milk, cheese, wool, meat
pig	meat (ham, bacon, pork chops)

For Sale!

Mooving sale! Retired farmer must sell barnyard animals. Needs to find a good home for milk-producing animal and her offspring. Won blue ribbons at County Fair. Both are white with black spots. Make me an offer. Call 555-5934.

CASE #
9

What is for sale?

©2002 by Evan-Moor Corp. Clues to Comprehension, Grades 3–4 • EMC 2721

Down on the Farm

1. Choose the best pair of words to complete this sentence:

A **calf** is to a **cow** as a _____ is to a _____ .

horn / bull	kitten / puppy
moth / butterfly	piglet / sow

2. Which of these is <u>not</u> a compound word?

barnyard   fairgrounds   milkmaid   tractor

3. Circle the word that does <u>not</u> belong.

cheese   crackers   cream   yogurt

4. Which word is a synonym for **offspring**?

baby   officer   parent   stream

5. On the back of this page, draw a picture of a farm animal that you would like to own. Use these lines to write about it.

_____

_____

_____

_____

©2002 by Evan-Moor Corp.

Note: This page may be reproduced for student use.

Geographical Organizer

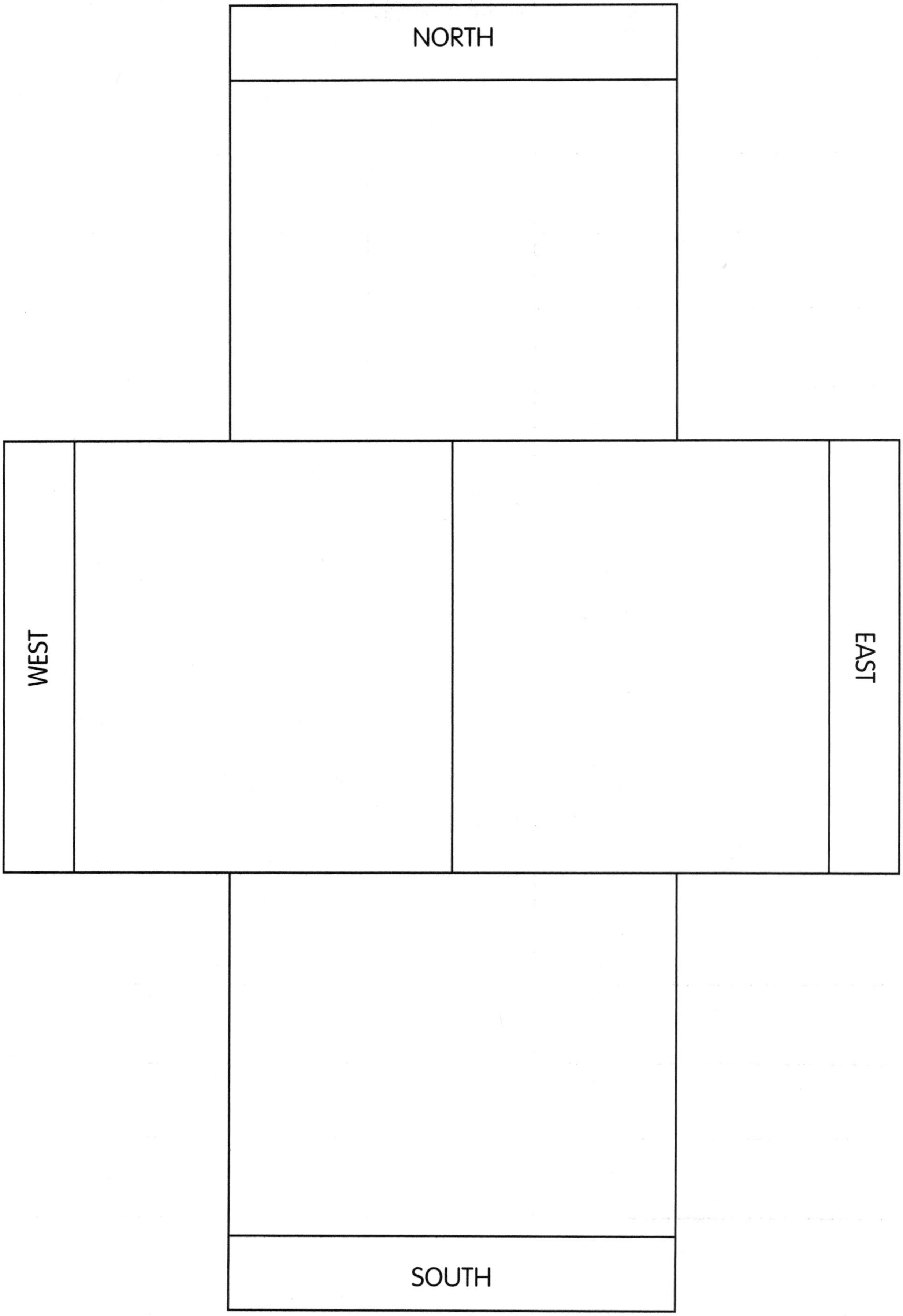

NORTH

WEST

EAST

SOUTH

©2002 by Evan-Moor Corp.
Clues to Comprehension, Grades 3–4 • EMC 2721

Note: This page may be reproduced for student use.

Topic, Subcategories, & Details

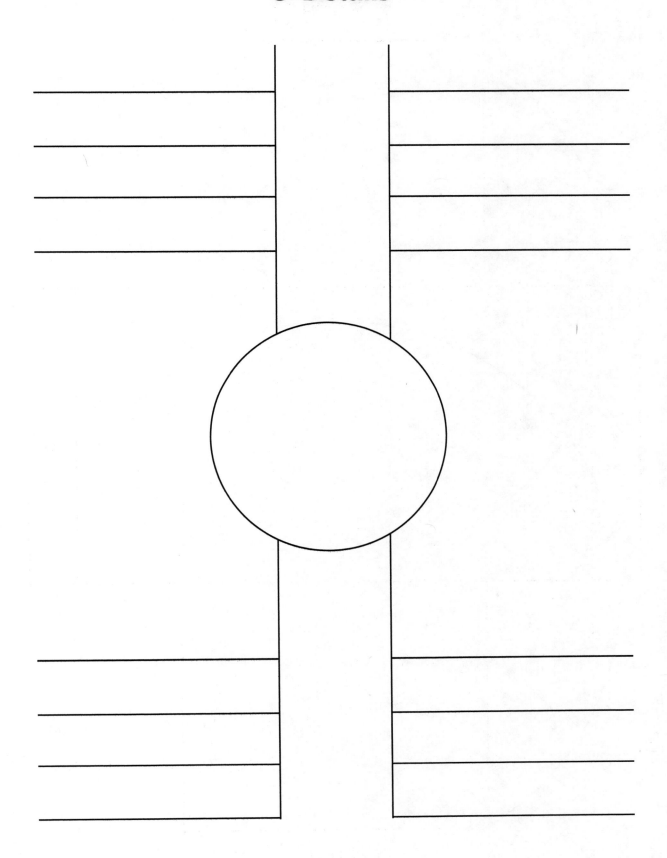

2-Part Venn Diagram

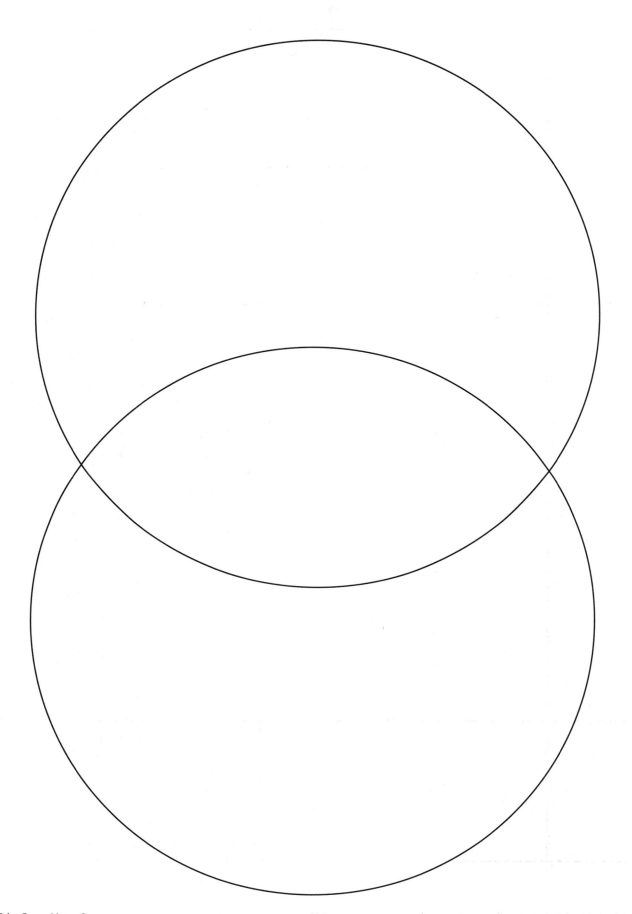

Note: This page may be reproduced for student use.

Attribute Chart

Note: This page may be reproduced for student use.

©2002 by Evan-Moor Corp.

Clues to Comprehension, Grades 3–4 • EMC 2721

Note: This page may be reproduced for student use.

T-Chart

Definition/Example
Organizer

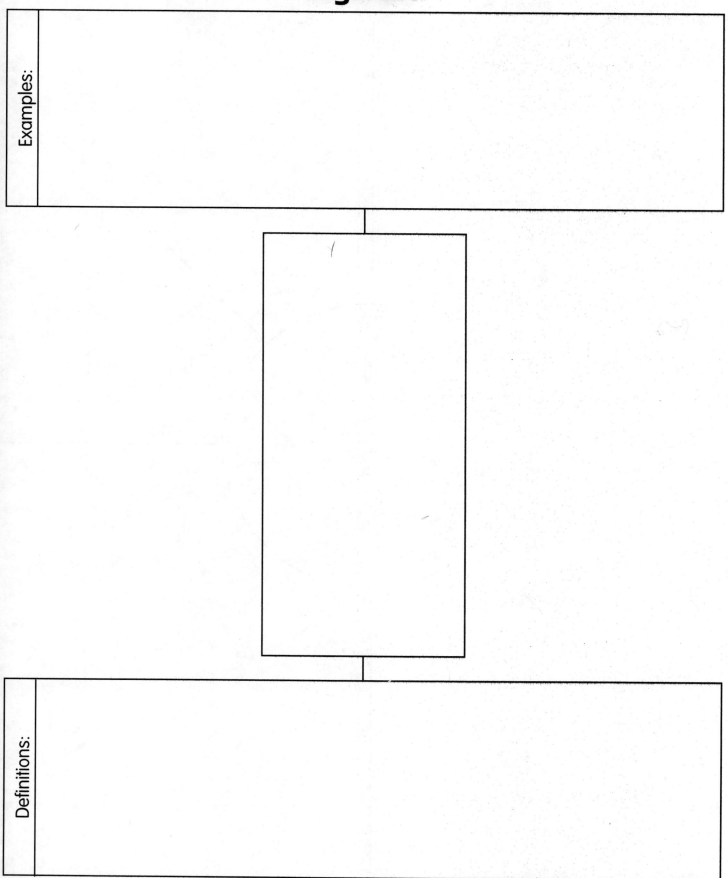

Examples:

Definitions:

©2002 by Evan-Moor Corp.

Clues to Comprehension, Grades 3–4 • EMC 2721

Note: This page may be reproduced for student use.

Topic & Details
Organizer

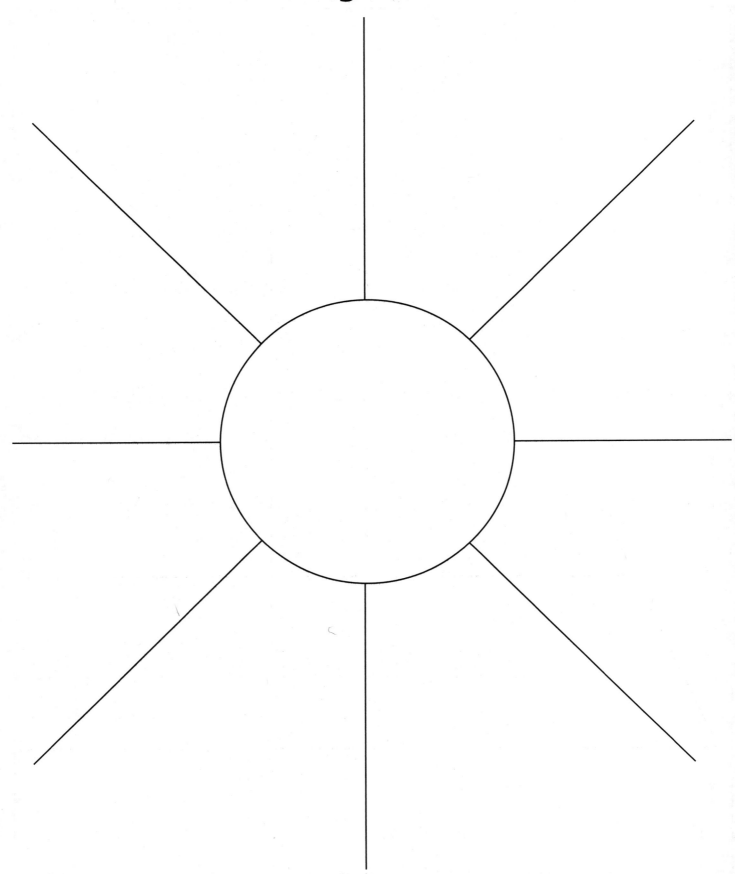

Note: This page may be reproduced for student use.

Food Pyramid

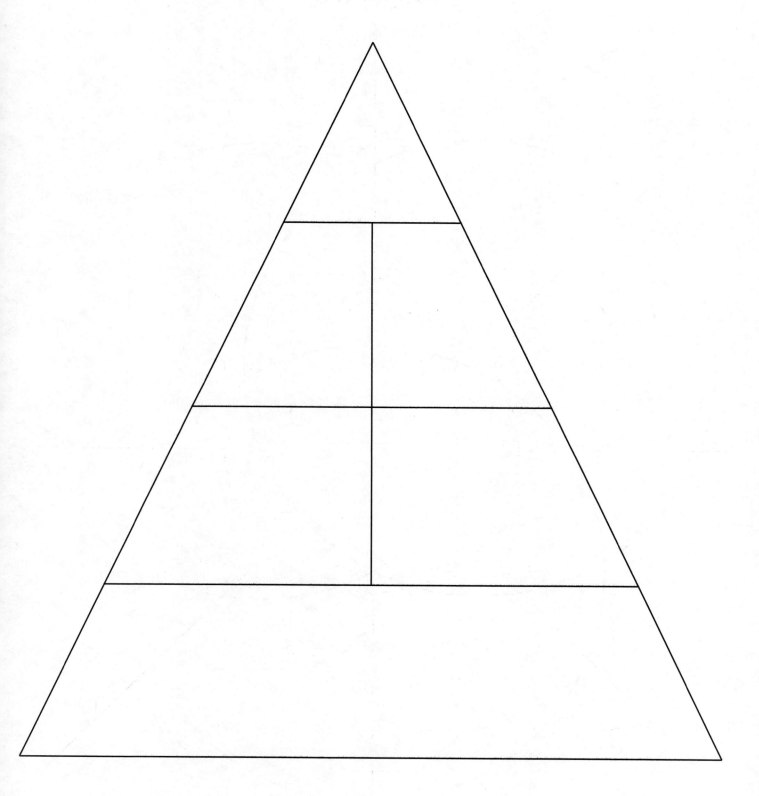

©2002 by Evan-Moor Corp.

Clues to Comprehension, Grades 3–4 • EMC 2721

Note: This page may be reproduced for student use.

3-Part Venn Diagram

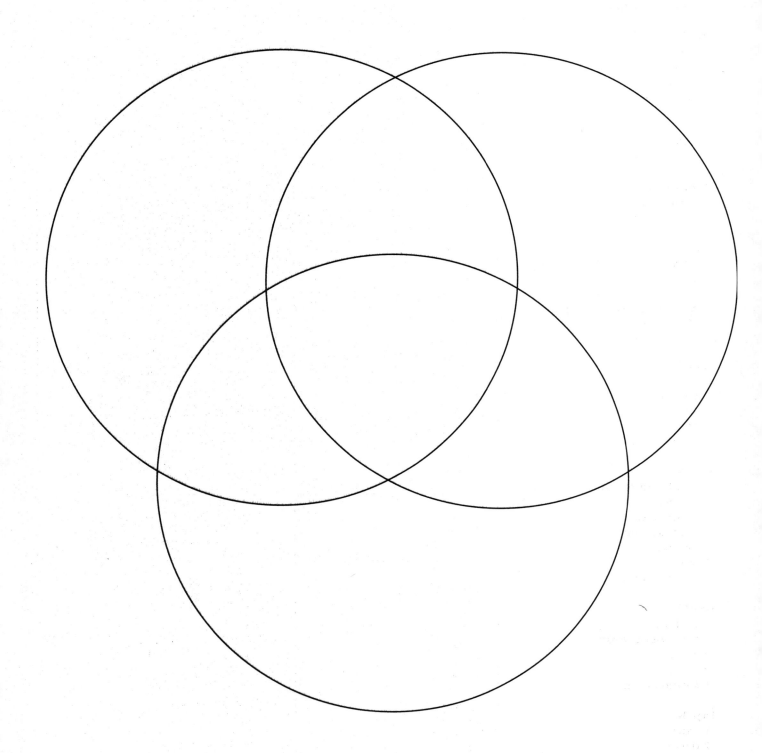

©2002 by Evan-Moor Corp.

Clues to Comprehension, Grades 3–4 • EMC 2721

Answer Key

Page 12
1. path
2. west
3. backpack
4. north
5. Answers will vary.

Page 15
1. in the fireplace
2. Arctic Circle
3. smoke
4. ties
5. Answers will vary.

Page 18
1. Sam rode a horse.
2. top
3. wide
4. Thanksgiving
5. Answers will vary.

Page 21
1. the president
2. disguise
3. wild
4. Accept all appropriate responses, including boom, doom, loom, etc.; bloom, fume, etc.
5. Answers will vary.

Page 24
1. coupons
2. a spoon
3. dull
4. skin
5. Answers will vary.

Page 27
1. keep it and not tell anybody
2. an apple
   a piece of gum
   a postage stamp
3. show proof
4. bank
5. Answers will vary.

Page 31
1. a hula-hoop
2. "Pop Goes the Weasel"
3. a cube
4. remote-control
5. Answers will vary.

Page 34
1. paper
2. circular
3. remote-control robots

Page 34 (continued)
4. chain
5. Answers will vary.

Page 37
1. a player on a baseball team
   a container to hold and pour liquid
2. hill
3. autograph
4. goalie
5. Answers will vary.

Page 40
1. metal
2. dining hall
3. cupcakes
4. suitcase
5. Answers will vary.

Page 43
1. The string broke.
2. short
3. cloth
4. skis
5. Answers will vary.

Page 46
1. on the beach
2. Accept all appropriate responses, including naught, taught, etc.; bought, thought, etc.; cot, dot, spot, trot, etc.
3. thick
4. frogs
5. Answers will vary.

Page 49
1. inside the barn
2. Accept all appropriate responses, including bull, full, pull.
3. fuzzy
4. shoes
5. Answers will vary.

Page 52
1. outside the house
2. Accept all appropriate responses, including die, lie, tie, etc.; by, my, fry, spy, etc.; high, sigh, etc.; buy, guy, etc.; bye, dye, rye, etc.
3. good
4. necklace
5. Answers will vary.

Page 55
1. He'll have to buy a new one.
2. Accept all appropriate responses, including cool, drool, fool, tool, yule, etc.
3. the leader of a country

Page 55 (continued)
4. pole
5. Answers will vary.

Page 59
1. talk with aliens
2. sink
3. glider
4. orbiting
5. Answers will vary.

Page 62
1. someone is crying
2. slow
3. hose
4. a person you can count on
5. Answers will vary.

Page 65
1. helping people buy books
2. find
3. novel
4. "Shut up!"
5. Answers will vary.

Page 68
1. sleepy
2. ir-
3. submarine
4. Accept all appropriate responses, including big, enormous, gigantic, huge, king-size, mammoth, etc.
5. Answers will vary.

Page 71
1. garden
2. un-
3. tray
4. Accept all appropriate responses, including bean, Dean, mean, etc.; green, sheen, queen, etc.; gene, scene, etc.
5. Answers will vary.

Page 74
1. try out
2. ability
3. book
4. Accept all appropriate responses, including bought, fought, thought, etc.; cot, dot, tot, etc.; caught, taught, etc.
5. Answers will vary.

Page 77
1. a blind person
2. cowardly
3. snorkel
4. Accept all appropriate responses, including

Page 77 (continued)

dole, hole, etc.; coal, goal, shoal, etc.; bowl, troll, etc.

5. Answers will vary.

Page 80

1. electronic appliances
2. thrilling
3. cameras
4. Accept all appropriate responses, including carry, marry, etc.; dairy, fairy, etc.; merry, cherry, etc.; wary, very, etc.
5. Answers will vary.

Page 83

1. using the Internet
2. responsibilities
3. calling card
4. Accept all appropriate responses, including bash, dash, stash, trash, etc.
5. Answers will vary.

Page 87

1. like to do everything themselves
2. filthy
3. sheets
4. Accept all appropriate responses, including bean, Dean, mean, etc.; seen, teen, etc.; gene, scene, etc.
5. Answers will vary.

Page 90

1. illusions
2. dis-
3. turkey
4. Accept all appropriate responses, including Dick, kick, click, slick, thick, etc.
5. Answers will vary.

Page 93

1. dinner
2. route
3. rocket
4. re-
5. Answers will vary.

Page 96

1. teach
2. veterinarian/animals
3. tail
4. dis-
5. Answers will vary.

Page 99

1. very scared
2. helper
3. start a fire

Page 99 (continued)

4. un-
5. Answers will vary.

Page 102

1. librarian/library
2. frosting
3. stew
4. Accept all appropriate responses, including bake, fake, etc.; flake, shake, etc.; break
5. Answers will vary.

Page 105

1. train
2. race
3. fold
4. Accept all appropriate responses, including bog, cog, fog, etc.; flog, grog, etc.
5. Answers will vary.

Page 109

1. frost
2. freeze
3. cane
4. Accept all appropriate responses, including bow, tow, show, throw, etc.; doe, toe, etc.; dough, though, etc.
5. Answers will vary.

Page 112

1. lemon
2. dinner/evening
3. pancake
4. Accept all appropriate responses, including dumb, thumb, etc.; bum, mum, strum, etc.; come, some, etc.
5. Answers will vary.

Page 115

1. sleep
2. bed/bedroom
3. television
4. Accept all appropriate responses, including buddy, muddy, ruddy, etc.
5. Answers will vary.

Page 118

1. illuminate
2. brightness
3. match
4. Accept all appropriate responses, including fight, might, etc.; bright, height; bite, kite, etc.
5. Answers will vary.

Page 121

1. job
2. It's for a right-handed person.
3. backyard
4. Accept all appropriate responses, including coal, goal, shoal, etc.; dole, hole, stole, etc.; boll, stroll, etc.
5. Answers will vary.

Page 124

1. pet
2. It has short ears.
3. mustache
4. darling
5. Answers will vary.

Page 127

1. brass
2. noisy
3. trumpet
4. Accept all appropriate responses, including ding, king, sing, etc.; bring, swing, etc.
5. Answers will vary.

Page 130

1. make dinner
2. if there's a fire
3. uncle
4. early
5. Answers will vary.

Page 133

1. piglet/sow
2. tractor
3. crackers
4. baby
5. Answers will vary.